Penguin Grammar Workbook 2 Pre-Intermediate

Edward Woods

Series Editor: Edward Woods

 C000166092

CONTENTS

PENGUIN BOOKS

Published by the Penguin Group
Penguin Books Ltd, 27 Wrights Lane, London W8 5TZ, England
Penguin Putnam Inc., 375 Hudson Street, New York, New York 10014, USA
Penguin Books Australia Ltd, Ringwood, Victoria, Australia
Penguin Books Canada Ltd, 10 Alcorn Avenue, Toronto, Ontario, Canada M4V 3B2
Penguin Books (NZ) Ltd, 182–190 Wairau Road, Auckland 10, New Zealand

Penguin Books Ltd, Registered Offices: Harmondsworth, Middlesex, England

Published by Penguin Books 1998
10 9 8 7 6 5 4 3 2

Illustration on page 45 by Bob Harvey, Pennant Illustration
and illustrations on pages 46 and 64 by Chris Chaisty

Set in Times and Helvetica
Printed and bound by the Bath Press Colourbooks, Glasgow

Introduction

Penguin Grammar Workbook 2 is for students who have been learning English for a short time and who are already able to use some basic grammatical structures. They are not yet preparing for exams such as the Cambridge First Certificate.

WHY IS GRAMMAR IMPORTANT?

Many people think that grammar is not important because people can understand them even when they make mistakes. However when you make mistakes, the listener has to be very careful about what you are saying. If you are always making mistakes, the other person will soon get tired of listening to you.

PENGUIN GRAMMAR WORKBOOK 2

The aim of the *Workbook* is to provide you with a lot of practice work to improve your use of grammar. The *Workbook* is divided into four sections.

The 45 units in the book cover all the important basic grammatical structures to help you to use English well. In addition to practising the way a structure is formed, there is also practice with how it is used.

A typical unit

1 Explanation Box Here you will find examples of the structure and short explanations of how it is formed and when it is used. In some cases, where the unit is comparing the use of two different structures, e.g. the present simple and the present continuous tenses (Unit 3), we focus on the different uses of the two structures, showing how they are used to mean different things.

2 Practice Exercises Most of the units have five exercises. The first three are for you to practise the form and the last two are to practise the use. The last two are often dialogues, short stories or are task based.

Where there is a lot of information, e.g. *some*, *any*, *no* (Unit 28), this is divided into two parts – some at the beginning and the rest after Exercise 3. In these cases, Exercises 1, 2 and 3 practise what is in the first box. Exercises 4 and 5 practise what is in the second box.

Testing your grammar

At the end of each section, there is a Revision Test for the section. The items are arranged in small groups. At the top of each group is an indication of which units they are testing, e.g. in Revision Test 1, you will see Units 1–11. In this way, you can see quickly what kinds of mistakes you are making and where you can find the information to help you and get more practice.

At the end of the book, there is an Exit Test. Again, the items are grouped according to the units they are testing. When you have done the Exit Test, you will see if you are ready to go on to *Workbook 3*.

The Answer Key

In the centre of the book, you will find the Answer Key for all the exercises and tests in the book. You can take this out of the book if you wish.

The End of the Book

At the end of the book, there are three sections to help you.
1 Irregular Verbs: this is a list of the most common irregular verbs, giving the infinitive, the simple past and the past participle.
2 Punctuation: this gives you information on when to use capital letters, commas and full stops.
3 Spelling: this is information to help you with plural and comparative forms.

FOR THE STUDENT

You can use this book to work on your own to improve your use of grammar. You can work through the book from the beginning. Many of you will want to spend more time practising the structures you find difficult. The Contents page at the beginning of the book will tell you where to find the grammatical structures you want.

Always read the explanation box carefully before doing the practice exercises. It is not necessary to do every exercise at once. At first, you should do only one or two. Go back and do the other exercises at a later date. This will give you extra practice when you feel you need it.

Some of the exercises are in the form of dialogues (Unit 3, Exercise 4). On these occasions you can practise speaking the dialogue with a friend.

FOR THE TEACHER

You can use this book as a Grammar Course book or as a supplementary book to give your students extra practice when they need it. It will also be useful for homework tasks.

In the classroom, the exercises which are in the form of dialogues (e.g. Unit 43, Exercise 5) can be used for role-play and pair work. There are also exercises, (e.g. Unit 33, Exercise 3) which can be used as group work tasks.

UNIT 1 Present Simple
I work

FORM

PRESENT SIMPLE
This is how we form the present simple.
Positive

| I/You/We/They | work |
| He/She/It | works |

Note:
Add s for he/she/it.
But:
1 For verbs ending in y after a consonant,
change y to ie and add s
cry – he cries   fly – she flies
2 Verbs ending with a vowel, add es
go – he goes   do – she does
Negative
Put do not after the subject and use infinitive form

| I/You/We/They | do not (don't) | work |
| He/She/It | does not (doesn't) | work |

Note:
We usually use the short form, don't or doesn't.

Question
1 Put do before the subject and then use infinitive form

| Do | I/you/we/they | work? |
| Does | he/she/it | work? |

2 With questions words Who or What:
When these words refer to the subject of the sentence,
we do not use the auxiliary do in the question
Who lives in that house?
3 With question words Which and What:
When these words are followed by a noun which is the
subject of the sentence, we do not use the auxiliary do
in the question
Which dress costs £500?
Note:
Use Which when we know what choices there are.
Use What when there are a lot of choices.
Note:
Put adverbs of frequency – always, usually, often,
sometimes, never, etc. – before the main verb:
They always work late.

1 Write the correct form

Write the correct form of the verb (positive, negative or
question).
Examples:
Richard always (work) on Sundays.
Richard always works on Sundays.
Victor (not play) football very well.
Victor doesn't play football very well.
(like) John and Mary Chinese food?
Do John and Mary like Chinese food?
Where (work) David?
Where does David work?

1 (Run) lions very fast?
2 Camels often (go) for days without water.
3 In some countries, the people (not eat) pork.
4 How much (cost) a Rolls-Royce?
5 Fred always (buy) Japanese cars.
6 What films (like) you?
7 Alice (not live) here any more.
8 (love) you me?
9 He's very rich. He (not need) any money.
10 The sun (rise) in the east.
11 We sometimes (have) parties.
12 (have) he a television?
13 Who (live) in this house?
14 (like) she playing sport?
15 They usually (go) home at Christmas.

2 Write the correct form

John is meeting Jill for the first time. Put the verbs in
the correct form.

John:	Hello! Nice to meet you!
Jill:	Yes, my name's Jill. What's yours?
John:	John. Where (**1** live) you?
Jill:	I (**2** live) in Bristol.
John:	So do I. (**3** like) you Bristol?
Jill:	Yes. What (**4** do) you?
John:	I (**5** teach). And you?
Jill:	I (**6** sell) flowers. But I (**7** not like) selling flowers.
John:	Why not?
Jill:	I (**8** want) to be an actor.
John:	(**9** Prefer) you TV or the theatre?
Jill:	Oh, the theatre. What (**10** teach) you?
John:	Maths. It's very boring.

UNIT 2 Present Continuous
I am working

FORM

PRESENT CONTINUOUS
Do you remember how we form the present continuous?
Positive

I	am ('m)	working
you/we/they	are ('re)	working
he/she/it	is ('s)	working

Note:
We usually use the short forms, *'m, 're, or 's.*
Negative

I	am not (I'm not)	working
you/we/they	are not (aren't)	working
he/she/it	is not (isn't)	working

Note:
We usually use the short forms.
Question

Am	I	working?
Are	you/we/they	working?
Is	he/she/it	working?

Note:
The first person singular and plural (*I* and *we*) is rarely used for questions.

---

1 Write in the correct form of the verb

Example:
Robert and Clive (study) in Paris at the moment.
Robert and Clive *are studying* in Paris at the moment.

1 The birds (fly) to their winter home.
2 Detective Brown (look) for the thief.
3 William (write) an historical play.
4 Vincent (paint) a very beautiful picture.
5 Maria (travel) in Africa.
6 She (walk) across the whole continent.
7 You (wear) a beautiful dress.
8 The 'phone (ring)!
9 They (play) that loud music again!
10 Hurry up! It (rain). I (get) wet.
11 She (read) all Charles Dickens' books
12 Martin (run) very fast!

2 Write the negative form

Example:
The sun (shine) today.
The sun *isn't shining* today.

1 The dogs (fight) any more.
2 Oscar (write) another story.
3 Their best footballer (play) today.
4 The computer's broken. It (print).
5 The birds (fly) high today.
6 Don't worry! I'm all right. I (get) tired.
7 Tony (take) photographs of the princess at the moment.
8 The children are very happy. They (make) any noise.
9 Anne's only going to Mexico. She (sail) round the world.
10 We (live) in Egypt any more.
11 I can't ring anyone today. My phone (work).
12 I'm glad it (rain) today.

3 Make questions

Example:
He's living in Cambridge now. (Where)
Where's he living now?
She's selling her house.
Is she selling her house?

1 Charlie's studying Spanish at university. (What)
2 Jane's learning computer skills. (What)
3 Paul's playing tennis.
4 Yes, Sally and Rosie are still singing with a rock group.
5 David's meeting his girl-friend at the station. (Where)
6 Tony's teaching German at the university. (What)
7 We are now travelling at 200 kilometres an hour. (How fast)
8 Maria and Tim are doing their exams this week. (What)
9 They're building new houses by the sea. (Where)
10 They're showing a space adventure at that cinema. (What)
11 Jane is working in Hungary this year. (Where)
12 Alan is visiting one of his patients.
13 John is buying a new car. (What)
14 Tom and Anne are taking their holiday this month. (When)
15 Yes, they're leaving at 6 o'clock.

UNIT 3 — Present Simple v. Present Continuous
I work v. I am working

USE

PRESENT CONTINUOUS
1 When you're doing something for a short time, or there's been a change since the last meeting *I'm living in Manchester now.*
(Either the speaker won't stay in Manchester or the listener didn't know about the change of address.)
2 When you're doing something now
I'm listening to some music on the radio at the moment.
3 When something is happening now
It's raining a lot now.
4 With *Always* when someone often does something that makes you angry
She's always arriving late.

PRESENT SIMPLE
1 When you do something that will last a long time
I live in Manchester.
(The person expects to stay for a long time.)
2 When you do something often
I usually listen to music in the evenings.
3 When something happens regularly
It rains a lot in the autumn.
Note:
The present simple is often used with adverbs of frequency – *always*, *usually*, *often*, *sometimes*, *never*, etc. (*see* Unit 32) and with expressions showing frequency, such as *every Monday, once a month*, etc.
4 When you talk about a permanent state
The sun rises in the east.
Water boils at 100°C.

---

1 Write the correct form of the verb

Example:
Jenny and Mike (write) another book at the moment. They always (write) their books together.
Jenny and Mike are writing another book at the moment. They always write their books together.

1 Where's Tom? He (play) football. He (play) every Saturday afternoon.
2 Toucans (nest) in tree holes and (eat) birds' eggs.
3 Hurry up! The bus (come)!
4 Already? It usually (come) at twelve. It's only quarter to twelve now.
5 (eat) Peter dinner already? It's only six o'clock. He (usually not eat) until eight.
6 Look, it (snow)! Really? It never (snow) at this time of the year.
7 Today is 29th February and I (celebrate) my birthday. I only (celebrate) it every four years.
8 What (show) at the cinema this week? I'm not sure but they always (show) an adventure film in the school holidays.
9 It's ten o'clock, so my sister (go) to bed now, but I (get up). I (live) in England. Where (live) she?
10 Jumbo jets (carry) 500 passengers and (fly) 400 k.p.h. How long (take) it a jumbo to fly from London to New York?

2 Write sentences

Write sentences about the people in the table below.

Write what they usually do and what they are doing today. The first one has been done for you.

PERSON	USUALLY	TODAY
Harry	run in the park	stay in bed

Example:
Harry usually runs in the park, but today he's staying in bed.

PERSON	USUALLY	TODAY
1 John	go to the office	work at home
2 You	work late	leave early
3 Alan	meet his friend Betty	meet Sally
4 Sarah	have lunch at 12 o'clock	have lunch at 2 o'clock
5 I	drive my car to work	go by train
6 Lucy	wear a dress	wear trousers
7 Keith	catch a bus to work	catch a train
8 Kate and Dick	swim before breakfast	do their homework
9 Tony	spend the evening at home	go to a party
10 We	watch the late news on TV	listen to a radio play
11 Philip	eat meat	eat fish
12 They	play football	watch it on TV
13 She	read a book at lunch-time	read a magazine
14 Anne	phone her customers	visit them
15 I	walk home	take taxi

3 Write the correct form of the verb

The following sentences show a) what people generally do (a rule), or b) how life is changing (change). Decide which sentences are rules and which are changes. Write R or C in the box. Then write the correct form of the verb.

Example:

People (live) by rules. $\boxed{R}$ People live by rules.

Life (change) today. $\boxed{C}$ Life is changing today.

1 People (live) in houses above the ground. ☐
2 Now people (build) houses under the ground. ☐
3 Now people (buy) bicycles. ☐
4 Birds (fly) south in winter. ☐
5 People (drive) cars everywhere. ☐
6 Now some birds (stay) in Britain. ☐
7 Wild animals (live) in the country. ☐
8 People (like) to watch TV and (not go) to the cinema. ☐
9 Now some wild animals (come) into the cities. ☐
10 Now people (go) to the cinema ☐

What changes (happen) in your country?

4 Correct form of the verb

Underline the correct form of the verb. The first two have been done for you.

P.C. Smith: <u>What's she doing</u>?/What does she do?

P.C. Jones: <u>She's walking</u> /She walks towards the bank.

P.C. Smith: It's Thursday.

P.C. Jones: That's right. She usually (**1** is going/goes) to the bank on Friday.

P.C. Smith: Why (**2** is she going/does she go) there today?

P.C. Jones: I don't know. (**3** She's carrying/She carries) something.

P.C. Smith: She always (**4** is carrying/carries) a handbag.

P.C. Jones: It isn't a handbag.

P.C. Smith: What is it then?

P.C. Jones: I can't see. (**5** She's going/She goes) into the bank.

P.C. Smith: What's her job? (**6** What is she doing/does she do)?

P.C. Jones: She's a teacher.

P.C. Smith: A teacher?! Why (**7** are we following/do we follow) her then?

P.C. Jones: (**8** She's living/She lives) in a big house.

P.C. Smith: So do you.

P.C. Jones: But her house is in an expensive part of the town. Where (**9** is she finding/does she find) the money?

P.C. Smith: Banks?

P.C. Jones: Probably.

P.C. Smith: (**10** Is she robbing/Does she rob) banks?

P.C. Jones: Someone does. Someone (**11** is robbing/robs) the banks in this region.

P.C. Smith: So you think she's robbing the banks.

P.C. Jones: Wait and see. Here she is. (**12** She's running/she runs) from the bank with a large sack. Now people (**13** are coming/come) out of the bank. (**14** They're shouting/they shout). It's too late.

P.C. Smith: Let's go after her.

5 Write the correct form of the verb

Solve the riddles! What am I?

Riddle 1.

I usually (**1** stand) in the middle of a room. I (**2** have) four legs and I (**3** look) strong. At the moment, someone (**4** put) plates on top of me. Five people (**5** sit) round me. They (**6** wait) for dinner. (**7**) What am I?

Riddle 2.

I (**8** have) six legs. I (**9** fly) around rooms and I (**10** make) people frightened. Sometimes I (**11** hurt) people. I (**12** live) in warm weather. The cold weather (**13** kill) me. At the moment, I (**14** play) at the window. I (**15** try) to get outside to see the sun. A man (**16** attack) me. (**17**) What am I?

Riddle 3.

Now I (**18** run) down the street. I (**19** look) for my master. I always (**20** run) very fast. Now I can see my master and I (**21** make) a loud noise. A lot of people (**22** not like) the noise. I (**23** have) four legs and a hairy coat. Whenever I (**24** see) my master, I (**25** jump) on him. (**26**) What am I?

UNIT 4 Past Simple
I walked along the road

Form

PAST SIMPLE
Do you remember how we form the past simple?
Positive
1 Add -ed to the base verb
I open the door (present) becomes *I opened the door.*
But:
2 For verbs ending in *e*, just add *-d*
  arrive – I arrived
3 For verbs ending in *y* after a consonant change *y* to *i*
and add *-ed*
cry – I cried
Note:
There are many irregular verbs (see p. 84).
Negative
Put *did not* after the subject and then use the infinitive
form

I/You/We/They	did not (didn't)	see him.
He/She	did not (didn't)	see him.
It (the train)	did not (didn't)	arrive on time.

Note:
We usually use the short form, *didn't.*
Question
1 Put *did* before the subject and then use the infinitive
form.

Did I/you/we/they	arrive on time?
Did he/she/it	arrive on time?

Note:
Be careful with the verb *to be.*
Was she frightened?
2 When Who or What refer to the subject of the sentence, we do not use the auxiliary *did* in the question.
Who lived in that house?

---

1 Write the correct form

Write the correct past form of the verb (positive or negative). Be careful! Some of the verbs are irregular.
Examples:
Derek (lose) his passport in Rome.
Derek *lost* his passport in Rome.
John (not remember) much about the film.
John *didn't remember* much about the film.

1 In 1492, Columbus (discover) America.
2 He (go) there with a crew from Spain.
3 They (find) tobacco in America.
4 They (bring) it back to Europe.
5 Margaret (not look) very happy at the party.
6 She (not talk) to anybody.
7 Last year, my friends (try) to fly round the world in a balloon.
8 My friend (not win) a million. He only (win) a thousand pounds.
9 Last year, a man (buy) a painting for $30 million.
10 Alfred (make) a beautiful table for Anna.

2 Write the correct form of the verb

Write the correct past form of the verb in these verses:

1 There (be) a young lady of Kew
  Who (not know) what to do,
  So she (lie) in bed
  Until she (be) dead,
  That sad young lady of Kew.

2 There (be) three young men on a flight
  From New York to Rio by night.
  As the 'plane (climb) higher,
  One (start) a fire,
  And (give) both of the others a fright.

3 Write questions

Read the story below and then write the correct questions.

Last year Mary went to Greece for a holiday. There she met a nice young man, who was a bank clerk in Athens. They went to the beach every day and most evenings they went to the disco. She enjoyed herself very much. He promised to write to her when she went home. In England she waited but she didn't get any letters from him. Finally she wrote to him. After two weeks she got a letter from Greece. But it wasn't from her friend. It was from his wife.

Example:
(What/Mary/last year) *What did Mary do last year?*

1 (Who/she/meet) ....
2 (What/his job) ....
3 (What/they/do) ....
4 (What/he/promise) ....
5 (What/she/do/when she got home) ....
6 (Who/write/first letter) ....
7 (What/happen/after two weeks) ....
8 (Who/write/that letter) ....

Past Continuous
I was walking along the road

FORM

PAST CONTINUOUS
Do you remember how we form the past continuous

Positive

| I/he/she/it | was | working |
| you/we/they | were | working |

Negative

| I/he/she/it | was not (wasn't) | working |
| You/we/they | were not (weren't) | working |

Note.
We usually use the short form, *wasn't* or *weren't*.

Question

| Was | I/he/she/it | working? |
| Were | you/we/they | working? |

1 Write the correct form

Write the correct form of the verb (positive, negative or question).

Example:
He (live) in Moscow when I saw him.
He *was living* in Moscow when I saw him.

1 I (watch) television last night.
2 Jane (study) for her exams all through the spring.
3 Peter (play) tennis when he met Daisy.
4 (Stay) you in this hotel last year? All the waiters know you.
5 We (not wait) for the boss at the station.
6 We (look) at the new, fast trains.
7 (Speak) you to Jim on the 'phone just now?
8 No. I (talk) to my brother.
9 Yesterday morning, Mary (clean) the house.
10 John (check) the car engine.

2 Write the correct form of the verb

Yesterday there was an accident at the cross roads between a big car and a small car. The police are interviewing a man who saw the accident. Write the correct form of the verb. The first one has been done for you.

Example:

P.C. Brown: Now, sir, what (do) you at the time?
Now, sir, what *were you doing* at the time?

Mr Jones: I (1 cross) the road at the junction.
P.C. Brown: You (2 cross) the road, sir.
Mr Jones: Yes. No cars (3 come). The road was empty.
P.C. Brown: Did you see the big, red car?
Mr Jones: Yes. It (4 race) very fast down the hill. And I could see the small, black car. It (5 come) along the road at the bottom of the hill. It (6 go) very fast, too.
P.C. Brown: Were there other people in the street?
Mr Jones: Yes, there were a lot of people. I saw Mary Rowland and Jill Hird. They (7 look) at the cinema poster. Mr and Mrs Smith (8 have) coffee in that corner café. A man (9 ride) a bicycle.
P.C. Brown: (10 pay) he attention to the road?
Mr Jones: I don't think so. But I think the accident was caused by the dog.
P.C. Brown: The dog?
Mr Jones: Yes, a dog (11 run) across the road. Its owner (12 shout) at it.
P.C. Brown: What (13 shout) the owner?
Mr Jones: She (14 tell) the dog to stop.
P.C. Brown: I see. (15 go) the car fast?
Mr Jones: Yes. I told you so.
P.C. Brown: Was there anyone else in the street?
Mr Jones: Yes. There was Joe Wright. He's always there. He (16 sell) newspapers. And there was a man at his shop. The man (17 buy) a newspaper. They all saw the accident.
P.C. Brown: I (18 talk) to Joe Wright this morning. He didn't see the accident. He only heard it. Now why (19 cross) you the road then? Didn't you see the cars?
Mr Jones: Of course. But no cars (20 come) when I looked.
P.C. Brown: Thank you, Mr Jones. That's all.

UNIT 6 Past Simple v. Past Continuous
I walked along the road v. I was walking along the road

USE

PAST SIMPLE
1 For something finished in the past
I read a book last night.
(You finished the book.)
2 For something which is the main interest
I lived in Rome from 1988 – 1990.
3 For a completed action
John came round.
PAST CONTINUOUS
1 For something in the past which may or may not be finished
I was reading a book last night.
(It is not certain if you finished the book.)

2 For something which is not the main interest
I was living in Rome from 1988–1990, but I didn't see the fire.
(The fire is important here.)
3 For an action which is interrupted
I was watching TV, when John came round.
or
While I was watching TV John came round.
4 For actions which were happening at the same time, where the speaker is focusing on the actions and not on when they happened
While you were cooking dinner, I was playing tennis.

---

1 **Write the correct form of the verb**

Example:
I met Tom, when I (walk) in the park. (interrupted)
I met Tom, when I *was walking* in the park.
Sally (drive) for the whole journey. (finished)
Sally *drove* for the whole journey.

1 Gerry (build) his house last summer. (unfinished)
2 The cat (stay) out all night. (finished)
3 I was shopping in Manchester, when I (hear) the news. (interrupted)
4 Peter (live) in Cardiff all his life. (finished)
5 They were buying a computer, when the thieves (come) into the shop. (interrupted)
6 The music (play) so I didn't hear the telephone. (interrupted)
7 The lion (come) slowly, while the antelope was eating, (interrupted)
8 While they (put) up the tent, a bear approached the camp. (interrupted)
9 The birds were flying very high, when someone (shoot) at them. (interrupted)
10 We (drive) to the hospital when the baby was born. (interrupted).

2 **Write the correct form of the verb.**

Example:
I (not see) Gerry, when I (walk) in the park.
I *didn't see* Gerry, when I *was walking* in the park.

1 While she (do) her homework, her father (come) home.

2 When David (see) Tom, he (not work), he (sleep) at his desk.
3 The burglar (come) while they (play) some loud music.
4 They (not hear) the burglar because they (play) the music too loudly.
5 The dog (bark), but nobody (come).
6 I (watch) TV when my aunt (arrive).
7 He (study) at Oxford when the war (begin).
8 The lion (not hunt) when the man (shoot) it.
9 We (play) cards when the fire (start).
10 He (give) her the ring as the train (leave).

3 **Write two questions for each statement**

Example:
While David was reading a book, he heard a shout in the next room.
What was David doing when he heard a shout in the next room?
What did David hear while he was reading?

1 They saw the monkeys while they were visiting the zoo.
2 Joan hurt her leg while she was climbing in the mountains.
3 We bought this perfume while we were staying in Paris.
4 Charlie met some old friends while he was working in Spain.
5 Richard was sleeping when the burglars came in.
6 The swan attacked them while they were fishing in the canal.

7 While they were playing an important football match, the manager sold the club.
8 While Simon was swimming in the river, his friend George took his clothes away.
9 Anne and Carl got married while they were living in Mexico.
10 Lots of people came to see him while he was painting the picture.

4 Complete the sentences

Complete the sentences, using the information in the table.

	Jane		John
1980–88	at school	1978–84	at school
1987	learn to drive	1985–89	live in London
1988–90	work in a shop in Berlin	1989	buy a house in Oxford
1991–94	study history	1990	marry Frances
1995	meet Andrew	1990–95	teach English in Oxford
1995–97	travel round the world with Andrew	1996–98	work in Scotland
1998	marry Andrew	1998	become a father

Example:
In 1979, John *was going to school.*
In 1998, Jane *married Andrew.*

1 In 1987, Jane . . . .
2 In 1988, John . . . .
3 In 1989, Jane . . . .
4 In 1989, John . . . .
5 In 1990, John . . . .
6 In 1992, Jane . . . .
7 In 1992, John . . . .
8 In 1995, Jane . . . .
9 In 1996, Jane . . . .
10 In 1998, John . . . .

5 Fill in the gaps

Complete the story below by filling in the gaps with one the verbs in the box. The first has been done for you.

come, follow, get out, go, hear, jump, laugh, phone, race, ring, see, stop, take.

It was two o'clock in the morning. The fire-engine *was racing* through the village. The men on it (**1**)...... and (**2**)...... the bell. A man in pyjamas (**3**)...... out of his house. He was tired and angry and he (**4**)...... the police.

Suddenly the men in the fire-engine (**5**)...... a noise. They (**6**)...... a police car. It (**7**)...... very fast. It (**8**)...... them. The police car (**9**)...... by the fire-engine. A policeman (**10**)...... of the car. The men (**11**)...... off the fire-engine. The policeman (**12**)...... them to the police station.

6 Write the correct form of the verb

Put the verbs in the correct tense.

1 At five forty-five
  a) Bob (leave) home.
  b) Harry (finish) his work.
  c) Jenny (close) her shop.

2 At six o'clock
  a) Bob (walk) along the road towards the town.
  b) Harry (meet) Jenny at the bus station.

3 At six fifteen
  a) Bob (buy) Jenny a box of chocolates.
  b) Harry and Jenny (wait) for a taxi.
  c) David (see) Harry and Jenny.

4 At six thirty
  a) Bob (meet) David.
  b) Harry and Jenny (arrive) at the Blue Moon restaurant.

5 At six forty-five
  a) David (tell) Bob about Harry and Jenny.

6 At seven o'clock
  a) Bob (feel) angry.
  b) Harry and Jenny (eat) at the restaurant.

7 At seven fifteen
  a) Bob (go) into the restaurant.
  b) Jenny (see) Bob and was frightened.

8 At seven thirty
  a) Bob, Jenny and Harry (shout) at each other.

9 At seven forty-five a) Bob (hit) Harry.
10 At eight o'clock
  a) Jenny (cry).
  b) The police (take) Bob to the police station.

UNIT 7 Talking About the Past: *used to*
I used to play in the park

FORM

Positive
I/You/We/He/She/It/They used to go.
Negative
I/You/We/He/She/It/They didn't use to go.
When I was a child, I didn't use to go to the park.
At university, she didn't use to study at all.
Note:
There is a negative form *Usedn't*, but this isn't used very often.
Question
Did I/You/We/He/She/It/They use to ...?
Did you use to go to the park as a child?
Did she use to study hard at university?
Note:
1 There is a question form *Used she to study ...?* but this isn't used very often.
2 With the negative and question forms, we don't put the *d* at the end of *used* with *did*.

USE
1 For events in the past which happened regularly or very often, but which no longer happen.
When I was a child, I used to play in the park.
At university, she used to study all night.
2 For situations in the past that lasted a long time, but which no longer apply.
I used to go to the school on the hill, but I go to the one in the town now.
There used to be a shop on the corner of that street, but it burnt down.
Note:
There is no specific time stated. When a time is mentioned, we use the simple past.
There was a shop on the corner of that street from 1920 to 1978.

1 Write the correct form

Write the correct form of used to (positive, negative or question).
Example:
He ... work late, but now he goes home early.
He used to work late, but now he goes home early.
... (you) live in Cairo?
Did you use to live in Cairo?

1   When I lived in Rome, I .... walk past the Forum every day.
2   There .... be a big sports field there, but now they've built a supermarket.
3   I .... (not) like her, but I do now.
4   I recognize you. .... (you) belong the film club?
5   When I was a child, we .... have lovely, hot summers.
6   Television's very boring now. There .... be some good plays on it.
7   When he was a student, he .... be very interested in politics.
8   What's happened? You .... (not) look sad all the time.
9   .... (you) know Mr Reginald Brown?
10 David .... (not) smoke, before he met those people at the boxing club.

2 Complete the story

Complete the story below with the correct form of used to *or simple past. The first two have been done for you.*

I *used to* live in Tokyo. I *lived* there for three years. It (**1** be) .... less polluted than it is now, but it was always very crowded. I (**2** go) .... to work by train every day. So on Sundays, I (**3** walk) .... in the parks to get some fresh air. There (**4** be) .... a lot of people in the park. I (**5** enjoy) .... watching all the people there. Then one Sunday, I (**6** see) .... a group of young people playing handball. They (**7** be) .... very happy there. I (**8** want) .... to join them. That was when I (**9** meet) .... my wife. After we (**10** get) .... married, we (**11** go) .... to the park to meet her friends. Then we (**12** leave) .... Tokyo. We still remember the park.

FORM

PRESENT PERFECT
For the present perfect we use *has/have* + the past participle.

1 The past participle is formed by adding *-ed* to the base verb
work – worked

2 When the verb ends in *-e*, just add *d*
arrive – arrived

3 When the verb ends in *-y*, change the *-y* to *-i* and add *-ed*
cry – cried

4 There are many irregular verbs, see p. 84
go – gone

Positive
I/You/We/They	have	worked
He/She/It	has	worked

In spoken language we use the short forms *'ve* and *'s*
I've arrived.
He's painted the picture.

Negative
Add *not* after *has* or *have*.
I/You/We/They	have	not worked
He/She/It	has	not arrived

She has not (hasn't) been to Turkey.

Question
Put *have* or *has* in front of the subject. (There is no short form.)
Have	I/you/we/they	arrived?
Has	he/she/it	arrived?

Have you paid the bill?

Note:
The present perfect form for *go* is *has gone*. This means the person is still away.
He has gone to Rome
(He is still in Rome.)
We also use *has been*. This means the person has come back.
He has been to Rome.
(We don't know when he was in Rome, but he is no longer in Rome.)

---

1 Complete the text

Complete the text below using the correct form of the verb. The first one has been done for you.

Ron (**1** visit) *has visited* India many times. Every year, since 1993, he (**2** return) to the same parts of the country and (**3** stay) in the same hotels. He (**4** make) many friends there. His friends in Madras (**5** buy) a small apartment for him. They (**6** always welcome) him back and some of them (**7** travel) with him. He (**8** climb) the great mountains in the north and (**9** see) the sun going down at the southern cape.

2 Complete the dialogues

Complete the dialogues below with the correct form of the present perfect.

Example:
(write) you that letter to Judy yet?
No, I (not do) it yet. But I (speak) to her mother on the 'phone.
Have you written that letter to Judy yet?
No, I haven't done it yet. But I've spoken to her mother on the 'phone.

1 (finish) you painting the house yet?
No, I (not do) it yet. But I (paint) all the inside walls.

2 I (not see) Geoffrey today.
He (go) to London.
(go) he there before?

3 Mary (break) those beautiful glasses.
(tell) she her mother? Her mother (not get) any more.

4 (bring) John the food?
No, he (not be) to the shop yet. He (lose) his money.

5 (pass) Daisy her exam?
Yes, she (win) a scholarship, but she (not decide) what to do.

3 Complete the dialogue

Complete the dialogue below by filling in the gaps with one of the verbs in the box. Use the present perfect. The first one has been done for you.

go hear know marry talk travel

Paul:	**1**..... you the news?
	Have you heard the news?
Rita:	No. What?
Paul:	Jane **2**..... Tom.
Rita:	(But they **3** never). .... about marriage.
Paul:	But they **4** ..... round the world.
Rita:	Not together.
Paul:	No. And they **5**..... to different places.
Rita:	**6**..... him long?
Paul:	Since school.

Past Simple v. Present Perfect
I saw him v. I have seen him

USE

PAST SIMPLE
1 When you know the time
I saw him last Tuesday.
2 You don't know the exact time, but can guess it
He met his wife in Rome.
(Here we don't know the exact time he met his wife, but we know when he was in Rome.)
3 Something finished in the past, even the recent past
The game finished three minutes ago.
4 With *for* when something is finished
They lived in Italy **for** *four years. They left Italy in 1996.*

PRESENT PERFECT
1 When something that began in the past is still happening
She has been a teacher here since 1975.
(she's still teaching here.)
2 Something that happened in the past, but we don't know when
Yes, she has read that book.
(We don't know when she read it.)
3 When we use it with *just* for something finished
The game has just finished.
Note:
This is used in British English only. In American English, they use the past simple: *I just saw him.*
4 With *since* or *for* when something is still happening
They have lived in Italy since 1993 (and still live there).
They have lived in Italy for four years (and still live there).
Note:
Since is followed by a time
since 1993/Tuesday/last night
for is followed by a period of time
for four years/three days/six hours

---

1 **Complete the table**

Complete the table by writing the past simple form and the past participle form. The first one has been done for you.

VERB	PAST SIMPLE	PAST PARTICIPLE
become	*became*	*become*
build	....	....
buy	....	....
come	....	....
fall	....	....
go	....	....
hang	....	....
have	....	....
hear	....	....
know	....	....
let	....	....
read	....	....
run	....	....
see	....	....
sell	....	....
sing	....	....
take	....	....
understand	....	....
win	....	....
write	....	....

2 **Write the correct form of the verb**

Write the correct form of the verb, past simple or present perfect.
Example:
They (buy) a new car.
They *have bought* a new car.

Sally (go) to the cinema last night.
Sally *went* to the cinema last night.
1 She (take) the dog to the vet last Tuesday.
2 Rupert (teach) at the summer school last August.
3 We must congratulate Sam. She (pass) all her exams with an 'A' grade.
4 I (see) just her going into the post office.
5 They (have) a new television since July.
6 They (buy) a new television in July.
7 John (be) head of the college for ten years. He wants to stay another three years.
8 That book is very good. Everyone in the family (read) it.
9 Greta (live) in Edinburgh for ten years and then (go) to Thailand.
10 David (paint) some pictures of flowers last year.
11 Anne (buy) a house in Madrid in 1990, and she (live) in Spain since then.
12 I (pass) all my exams last year.
13 She (meet) her husband at work.
14 Oh yes, I (visit) America many times, too.
15 I last (go) there in 1994.

3 Write the answers

Example:
Have you seen that film about the Space Wars?
Yes, *I have*. I *saw* it in January.

1 Have you been to the Taj Mahal?
   Yes, ... I .... there in 1994.
2 Have you ever seen the Queen?
   Yes, ... I .... her last May.
3 Have you ever built a house?
   No, ... But my father .... this one in 1952
4 Has she finished her work already?
   Yes, ... She .... it ten minutes ago.
5 Has David invited the Robinsons to his party?
   Yes, ... He .... them last week.
6 Have they been to Morocco?
   Yes, ... They .... there in 1995.
7 Has Brian ever flown in a balloon?
   No, ... But his wife .... in one two years ago.
8 Have you ever won the lottery?
   No, ... But my neighbour .... £3 million last September.
9. Has the TV play started yet?
   Yes, ... It .... ten minutes ago.
10 Have you finished that essay?
   Yes, ... I .... it yesterday.
11 Has Christine arrived?
   Yes, ... She .... two hours ago.
12 Have they ever had a dog?
   Yes, ... They .... for ten years.
13 Have you found your watch?
   Yes, ... I found it in my suitcase.
14 Has June ever visited her parents in France?
   No, ... But her brother .... them last month.
15 Have you seen that film yet?
   No, ... But my boyfriend .... it last night, and really liked it.

4 Write questions for the answers given:

Examples:
No, I haven't read it.
Have you read that book?
Sheila worked there in 1987.
When did Sheila work for the company?
Barry has lived in six different countries.
How many countries has Barry lived in?

1 No, I didn't see John when I was in Berlin.
2 I went to Cambridge by the A1 route.
3 Dolly last sang a popular song in 1996.

4 Yes, Pete and Dave have climbed all the hills in England.
5 Fred has written twelve crime books.
6 No, I didn't drive too fast.
7 John has sold all his 1960s records.
8 The telephone has rung three times for you.
9 I've waited here for two hours.
10 Yes, she won the swimming race.
11 No, Anne hasn't phoned yet.
12 I read all his books last summer.
13 They've been in the restaurant for two hours.
14 My father lives in Australia.
15 No, they haven't found a new house.

5 Complete the news item

Complete the news item below with the correct form of the verb. The first paragraph has been done for you.

'Here is the news from the galaxy.

Jago, our Supreme Ruler, (celebrate) *celebrated* his 25th anniversary as our ruler last Saturday. He (become) *became* our ruler in 2315 In twenty five years, he (make) *has made* the people of Lexef galaxy the richest and strongest in the universe.

Gado, the old ruler, (**1** be) ruler for forty years. He (**2** make) our galaxy very weak and poor. Gado (**3** take) money from the people and (**4** become) rich. There (**5** be not) enough food. Many hospitals (**6** close). Armies from the other galaxies often (**7** come) and (**8** fight) us.

Jago (**9** change) all that. Since 2326, we (**10** have) the biggest army in the universe. No one (**11** attack) Lexef since 2327. Then we (**12** beat) the army from Gamlish galaxy.

Since 2320, there (**13** be) enough food for everyone. Jago (**14** build) three thousand new hospitals. Crime (**15** fall) by 80 per cent.

Now we are the most advanced galaxy in the universe. In the last four years, the government (**16** connect) every house to the cyber-galactic-way-net. We can now communicate with each other whenever we like and in private. Gado (**17** not allow) people to communicate. Everyone (**18** be) afraid then. Now we are free. Long live Jago!'

Talking About the Future 1: *will/shall* v. *be going to*

I will see him v. I'm going to see him

FORM

Positive
1 *will* + base verb
I/You/We/He/She/It/They will see him
I'll see you next week.
Note:
For *I* and *we*, it is possible to use *shall*. Usually, in speech both *shall* and *will* are shortened to *'ll*. The negative for *shall* is *shan't*.
2 *Going* to + base verb
I'm   going to see him
You/We/They're   going to see him
He/She/It's   going to see him.
They're going to see him on Monday.
Negative
1 will not (won't) + base verb
I/You/We/He/She/It/They won't see him

2 *not going to* + base verb
I'm not   going to see him
You/We/They aren't   going to see him
He/She/It isn't   going to see him
Question
1 *will* + subject + base verb
Will I/you/we/he/she/it/they see him?
2 *be* + subject + *going to* + base verb
Am I   going to see him?
Are you/we/they   going to see him?
Is he/she/it   going to see him?
Note:
The question form is rarely used with first person singular (*I*).

USE

PREDICTIONS
1 We use *will* for general predictions
It'll be cold in January.
You'll like travelling through Malaysia.
2 We use *will* or *going to* for predictions where we have evidence
It's getting very cloudy, it's going to rain.
It's getting very cloudy, it'll rain soon.
INTENTIONS
For intentions, we can use either *will* or *going to*
I'll have my holiday in October.
She's going to have her holiday in October.
Notes:
1 When the main verb is *go*, we often use only the present continuous form
I'm going to Spain in January.

2 When the main verb is *come*, we don't use *going to*. We only use the present continuous form for *come*
I'm coming to see you on Sunday.
PROMISES AND OFFERS
We use *will* for promises and offers.
I'll come and visit you again tomorrow.
I'll help you all I can.
SUGGESTIONS
We use *shall* for suggestions
Shall we go to the cinema tonight?
Shall I start cooking the meal now?
REQUESTS
We use *will* for requests
Will you post this letter for me, please?

---

1 **Complete the dialogue**

Complete the dialogue with the correct form of going to. *The first one has been done for you.*
Mattie: Now, Tom. You (finish) at university in June. Now Tom. *You're going to finish* at university in June.
Tom: Yes. That's right.
Mattie: So, what (**1** do) you?
Tom: I (**2** travel) round the world.
Mattie: (**3** have) you enough money?
Tom: I think so. I (**4** get) a job in the summer and I (**5** save) some money. I (**6** not need) a lot of money.
Mattie: When (**7** start) you travelling?

Tom: In October. I (**8** sail) across the Atlantic to Brazil.
Mattie: (**9** buy) you a boat?
Tom: No. I (**10** work) on a ship.
Mattie: You (**11** have) an exciting time.

2 **Fill in the gaps**

Fill in the gaps with will ('ll) *or* won't.
Example:
We ..... be late.
We'll be late.

1 Next year I .... be twenty-four.
2 We .... have a new president in May.

3 I .... (not) be able to come next week.

4 It .... be very cold next winter.

5 It's very early. There .... (not) be anyone at home yet.

6 I .... learn to swim next year.

7 It's a horror film. He .... (not) like it.

8 She's very clever. She .... pass the exams easily.

9 He .... be head of the department soon.

10 They drive very fast. They .... have an accident.

3 Match the sentences

Match the sentences. The first has been done for you.

1 It's already five o'clock.   a) He's going to win the race.

2 I've booked my holiday.   b) It's going to rain.

3 That was thunder.   c) They're going to buy it.

4 That's a lovely house.   d) John's going to be late.

5 He's practising a lot.   e) She's going to see the doctor.

6 She's very ill and tired.   f) I'm going to visit friends in New York.

Why is going to *used in each of these sentences?*

1 *prediction with evidence*

2 . . . .

3 . . . .

4 . . . .

5 . . . .

6 . . . .

4 Match the sentences.

Match the sentences. The first has been done for you.

1 She's got a job in films.

2 The flight is at seven o'clock.

3 You can't go out. It's raining.

4 There's a good film on TV tonight.

5 You've got a lot to do.

6 I'm going to India.

a) Will you watch it?

b) Shall I help you?

c) She'll enjoy that.

d) I'll visit the Taj Mahal.

e) I'll be in New York by ten.

f) You'll get wet.

Why is will *used in these sentences?*

1 *general prediction*

2 . . . .

3 . . . .

4 . . . .

5 . . . .

6 . . . .

5 Choose the use

Read the sentences below, and choose which use of will *or* going to *(A–G) each shows.*

A general predictions **B** predictions with evidence **C** intentions **D** promises **E** offers **F** suggestions **G** requests

Example:

Will you help me with this exercise, please? G

1 Shall we go to the theatre tomorrow night? ☐

2 It's going to be a lovely day. Look at that clear sky.

3 She's going to Fiji for her holiday next year. ☐

4 The winner will be the first person to complete all the tasks in the right order.

5 I'll be there by ten on Friday.

6 It'll snow in January. ☐

7 I'll be in Italy this time next month, I hope. ☐

8 Shall I see you next week? ☐

9 Are we going to buy the house or not? ☐

10 Will you carry this for me? ☐

6 Write *will* or *going to*

Write will *or* going to *with the verbs in the sentences below.*

1 You (enjoy) that film.

2 The sky is clear tonight; it (be) cold.

3 She (visit) Greece in the Autumn.

4 She has promised that she (see) you next week.

5 I (talk) to her in the morning.

6 They (get married) in May.

7 He (be) an engineer.

8 They (be) here at nine.

9 I like hot countries, so I (like) Tunis.

10 She (borrow) the book from the library.

UNIT 11
Talking About the Future 2: Present Simple v. Present Continuous
The train arrives at five v. I'm seeing him at five

USE

PRESENT SIMPLE
1 For official times that are planned in a timetable or in the calendar
The train to Lancaster leaves at 9.35 a.m.
The course begins on 7th July.
2 For fixed dates
They celebrate their wedding anniversary in June.
Sunday's the 29th.
3 After *if* and time conjunctions, such as *when, after, before, as soon as*

You'll meet her if you get to the station before six o'clock.
I'll be home before he telephones.
They'll start work as soon as the material arrives.
PRESENT CONTINUOUS
For definite plans and arrangements
I'm starting work next week.
She's meeting the committee at five o'clock.
They're getting married in December.

---

1 Choose the use

Read the sentences below and choose which use (A, B or C) of the present simple each shows.
A official times
B fixed dates
C after IF and time conjunctions
Example:
The 'plane arrives at 6.30. [A]

1 School starts on 8th January. ☐
2 They'll meet when they get to Istanbul. ☐
3 We have English classes at two o'clock every afternoon. ☐
4 Don't be late! The bus leaves at eight. ☐
5 The royal visit is in July. ☐
6 The firework display starts at 10 o'clock. ☐
7 As soon as I get there, I'll send you a card. ☐
8 You parents will be angry if you come home late. ☐
9 Will you be able to finish the report before you go. ☐
10 Their flight gets in at 5.35. ☐

2 Write sentences

These are David's arrangements for the ten days between 17th and 27th June. Write ten sentences saying what he is doing.
Example:
On Sunday 17th June, in the morning, David's sailing on the river.

Sunday, 17th June

morning – sail on the river
2.30 p.m. – help Fred paint the kitchen

Monday, 18th June

11 a.m. – meet John Roberts
12.30 p.m. – have lunch with Andrew
6 p.m. – play tennis

Thursday, 21st June

evening – go to the theatre

Saturday, 23rd June

morning – do the garden
evening – go to Alice's party

Tuesday, 26th June

drive to London

Wednesday 27th June

8 a.m. – attend a business meeting
6 p.m. – return home.

1 _____

2 _____

3 _____

4 _____

5 _____

6 _____

7 _____

8 _____

9 _____

10 _____

3 Complete the sentences

Complete the sentences. Write the correct form of the verb, present simple or present continuous. Give the reason for your choice.

Example:
The train (arrive) at half-past seven.
The train arrives *at half-past seven. (*official time*)*
I (meet) June at four o'clock.
I'm meeting *June at four o'clock. (*definite plan*)*

1 Hurry up! The bus (leave) at two o'clock.
2 The new shop (open) next Tuesday.
3 John (have) a holiday in Miami this year.
4 They (give) Sarah a party for her birthday.
5 I (work) at home next week.
6 The exam results (come) in August.
7 The football match (start) at half-past two.
8 I (have) dinner with Simon tonight.
9 The restaurant (open) at seven.
10 She (leave) the job at the end of the week.
11 They (go) to the theatre tomorrow.
12 They (go) to the country at weekends.
13 We (have) steak tonight.
14 She (go) everywhere with John.
15 I (eat) my lunch at 12.30.
16 All the cinemas and the theatres (close) on Christmas Day.
17 Anne and I (take) a walk on Saturday afternoons.
18 This Saturday we (go) to the hills.
19 His car is fifteen years old. He (buy) a new one this month.
20 Come and say goodbye, Mary (leave) soon.

4 Complete the sentences

Complete these sentences by writing one of the verbs in the future with will, *and the other in the present simple.*
Example:
I (see) Richard when I (go) to Madrid.
I'll see *Richard when I* go *to Madrid.*

1 When I (see) Richard, I (tell) him about your new job.
2 If you (arrive) early, you (be able) to watch the parade.
3 The game (be) over before you (reach) the stadium.
4 They (sell) their house if they (find) a good buyer.
5 As soon as David (learn) the results of the exam, he (look) for a job.
6 When he (get) a job, he (buy) a house.
7 After he (buy) a house, he (get) a car.
8 If he (get) a car, he (learn) to drive.
9 After he (learn) to drive, he (visit) his girl-friend in Greece.
10 If he (go) to Greece, he (get) married.
11 If she (pass) her exams, she'll go to university.
12 When I (get) to work, I (phone) you.
13 After they (return) from India, they (take) a rest.
14 I stop work, if I (win) the lottery.
15 Dinner (be ready), when we (get) home.

5 Complete the dialogue

Greg and Sally are making plans for the weekend. Complete the dialogue with the correct form of the verb (present simple or present continuous).

Greg: What (**1** do) you on Saturday?
Sally: I (**2** go) to the theatre. Why?
Greg: I (**3** have) a party. I'd like you to come.
Sally: That's difficult. John (**4** buy) the tickets this afternoon.
Greg: Come afterwards. What time (**5** finish) the play?
Sally: I'm not sure. It (**6** start) at 7.30. It's about two hours long.
Greg: Then you could come at ten. It's important because I (**7** leave) for China on Monday.
Sally: Why (**8** go) you there?
Greg: I (**9** work) there for the next two years.
Sally: Two years. Then I (**10** come) for a holiday.

UNIT 12 Modals 1: *must / have to / need*

FORM

MUST
Positive
I/You/We/He/She/It/They must go
Negative
I/You/We/He/She/It/They must not (mustn't) go
Question
Must I/you/we/he/she/it/they go?

HAVE TO
Positive

| I/You/We/They | have to | go |
| he/she/it | has to | go |

Negative

| I/You/We/They | don't have to | go |
| He/She/It | doesn't have to | go |

Question

| Do I/you/we/they | have to | go? |
| Does he/she/it | have to | go? |

NEED
Positive

| I/You/We/They | need to go |
| He/She/It | needs to go |

Negative

I/You/We/They don't	need to go
or	
I/You/We/They	needn't go
He/She/It doesn't	need to go
or	
He/She/It	needn't go

Question

Do I/you/we/they	need to go?
or	Need I/you/we/they go?
Does he/she/it	need to go?
or	Need he/she/it go?

Notes:
1 Must has no past or future form. *Have to* and *need* have all tense forms.
2 Need is like *have to* in the positive form.
Need is like *have to* or *must* in the negative and question forms.

USE

OBLIGATION
(It's the law or there is an authority.)
Children must go to school. (It's the law.)
You have to do your homework tonight. (The teacher says so.)
NECESSITY
(It's necessary for personal reasons.)
I have to finish that work today. (I want to go on holiday tomorrow.)
Children need to go to school (so they can learn).

NOT OBLIGATORY/NOT NECESSARY
I don't have to finish that work today.
I don't need to finish that work today.
I needn't finish that work today.
NOT ALLOWED (FORBIDDEN)
You mustn't arrive late for work.

---

1 **Write the correct form of the verb**

Example:
They (must) do the work tonight.
They *must* do the work tonight.
She (have) visit her aunt next week.
She *has to* visit her aunt next week.
You (need) read that book. It will help you in the exam.
You *need to* read that book. It will help you in the exam.

1 You (not have) pay for them now.
2 (Need) they finish the painting today?
3 (Must) you catch the late train?
4 He (not must) see you here.
5 Everyone (have) eat.
6 (Have) we go there?
7 We (must) all leave the building immediately.
8 You (not need) book your seat for the theatre.
9 They're very rich. They (not have) work.
10 You (need) get a car. The public transport is bad.
11 It's raining. You (need) take an umbrella with you.
12 She (not have) to come in early every day.
13 You (must) find that money. It's mine!
14 I (need) at least eight hours sleep every night.
15 She (not need) to work so hard.

2 Complete the sentences

Complete the sentences with must *or* have (to).
Example:
Tom *must* write the essay before Friday.

1 Fred .... see his boss this morning.
2 Fred .... (not) to see his boss this morning.
3 .... Fred see his boss this morning?
4 We .... to get to work early.
5 We .... (not) to get to work early.
6 .... we to get to work early?
7 You .... buy some oranges.
8 You .... (not) buy any oranges.
9 I .... finish this exercise.
10 .... I to finish this exercise?
11 .... she to work this Saturday?
12 She .... work this Saturday.
13 Jenny .... pay her bills today.
14 Jenny .... (not) to pay her bills today.
15 .... Jenny to pay her bills today?

3 Complete the sentences

Complete the sentences with the correct form of need.

1 Fred .... see his boss this morning.
2 Fred .... (not) to see his boss this morning.
3 .... Fred see his boss this morning?
4 We .... get to work early.
5 We .... (not) to get to work early.
6 .... we to get to work early?
7 You .... buy some oranges.
8 You .... (not) buy any oranges.
9 I .... finish this exercise.
10 .... I to finish this exercise?
11 .... she to work this Saturday?
12 She .... to work this Saturday.
13 Jenny .... to pay her bills today.
14 Jenny .... (not) to pay her bills today.
15 .... Jenny to pay her bills today?

4 Write the correct form

*Write the correct form of the modal (*must/have *or* to/need*) for the use shown.*
Example:
You .... obey the school rules. (obligation)
You must *obey the school rules.*

1 Children .... go to school. (obligation)
2 You .... walk on the grass. (not allowed)

3 You .... have a passport when you go to another country. (obligation)
4 That's a nasty, deep cut. We .... clean it and bandage it. (necessity)
5. You .... wear heavy shoes on this floor. (not allowed)
6 You .... park your car here. (not allowed)
7 They .... get there early. (not obligatory)
8 Spacecraft .... travel at 28,000 miles an hour before they leave the earth. (necessity)
9 We .... take the exam this year. (not obligatory)
10 Librarians .... retire until they are 65 (not obligatory).
11 She .... take this medicine. (necessity)
12 Dogs .... stay outside this shop. (obligation)
13 You .... smoke in here. (not allowed)
14 He .... eat regularly. (obligation)
15 You .... to have a lot of money if you want to give up work. (necessity)

5 Rewrite these sentences

Rewrite these sentences using must, have to *or* need.
Example:
It's necessary to be rich to join.
You need to have/to be rich to join.

1 It's obligatory to arrive before eight o'clock.
2 It's obligatory to wear the correct clothes. You won't be admitted, if you don't.
3 It's not necessary to pay every time.
4 It is forbidden to bring your wife. Only men can come to the dinner.
5 It's necessary to buy a car if you live in the country.
6 It's not necessary to have your own horse.
7 It is forbidden to go on the course before a big race.
8 It's not necessary to live in the town.
9 It's forbidden to bring your own food into this restaurant.
10 It's obligatory to have lunch before half-past one.
11 It's necessary to wear formal clothes to this party.
12 It's forbidden to smoke in many restaurants now.
13 It's not necessary to buy all the books on this list.
14 It's forbidden to take photographs in here.
15 It's obligatory to pay before you go in.

FORM

CAN
Positive
I/You/We/He/She/It/They can do it
Negative
I/He/She/It/We/You/They cannot (can't) do it
Question
Can I/we/you/he/she/it/they do it?
COULD
Positive
I/You/We/He/She/It/They could do it
Negative
I/He/She/It/We/You/They could not (couldn't) do it
Question
Could I/we/you/he/she/it/they do it?
Note:
Generally *can* and *could* are different verbs and have no past or future form. However when they express ability or possibility, *could* is the past form of *can*. *Can* is used to express the future sometimes.
BE ABLE

Positive
I am able (I'm able) to do it
You/We/They are able ('re able) to do it
He/She/It is able to do it ('s able) to do it
Negative
I'm not able to do it
We/You/They aren't able to do it
He/She/It isn't able to do it
Question
Am I able to do it?
Are you/we/they able to do it?
Is he/she/it able to do it?
Notes:
1   The first person singular (I) is rarely used for questions.
2   *Be able to* has all tense forms.
They were able to do it.
She'll be able to do it.

USE

ABILITY
Lee can drive now.
Jane is very tall. She can touch the ceiling.
Notes:
1 In the present (or when there is future meaning) you can replace *can* with *be able to*.
Bob is a fast runner. He is able to run a mile in three minutes.
Bob is very fit. He'll be able to win easily.
2 Could is only used for past meaning.
Mary was very clever. She could do all the exercises in ten minutes.
POSSIBILITY
1 For general possibilities
There are ways you can help.
In the present, we can replace *can* with *could*
Note:
For the past form, we use *could + have +* past participle
There were ways you could have helped.
2 For specific possibilities
I have to spend my weekend with my parents. What could be worse?
With this meaning, we only use *could*. The past form is *could have*.
NOT ALLOWED (FORBIDDEN)
You can't park here.
Past:
You couldn't park here last week.

REQUESTS AND ASKING PERMISSION
Can/Could I borrow ten pounds? (request)
Can/Could I go out tonight? (asking permission)
Note:
Be able to is not used for this meaning.
Giving and Refusing Permission
Can/Could I go out tonight?
Yes, you can.
No, you can't.
Notes:
1 Only *can* is used in the answer.
2 *Be able to* is not used for this meaning.
Possible events
1 present
He could be in the garden now.
2 future
I could change my job next year.
3 past
She could have arrived at the wrong station.
Note:
Only *could* is used here.

1 Complete the sentences

Complete the sentences with can, could *or* be able.

Example: Mary was a very clever child. She *could* read at four years old.

1 John is very strong. He .... lift 28 kilos.
2 I arrived too late. The doors were closed. I .... (not) get in.
3 Because they are students, they .... to get cheap travel tickets.
4 I .... (not) to see him, because he was away on business.
5 I don't believe it. Nobody .... run five miles in six minutes.
6 Rosie felt very ill and .... (not) go to work.
7 In the future, you .... to have holidays on the moon.
8 They say cats .... see in the dark.
9 It was very cold in May and you .... (not) swim in the sea.
10 That car .... travel at 200 kph.

2 Complete the questions

Complete the questions with can, could *or* be able.

Example: (you) to speak Russian?
Are you able *to speak Russian?*

1 (you) to see the exhibition while you were in Rome?
2 (Penny) really speak six languages?
3 How (a man) live with 20,000 bees on him? I don't know, but Max Beck did in 1987.
4 (they really) to sell their house for £500,000 last year?
5 (you) see France from England on a clear day?
6 (people) go to the moon before 1969?
7 Where (you) see the sun set and the moon rise together?
8 How long (a man) to stay under water?
9 When (we) to see an eclipse of the sun again?
10 What (you) see when you were at the top of the mountain?

3 Complete the dialogue

Complete the dialogue with can, could *or* be able. *The first one is done for you.*

Maisie: Rob. *Could* you lend me £80, please?
Rob: No, I (1) .... (not). I'm sorry. Why do you want £80?
Maisie: So that I (2) .... buy a dress for the party tonight. I (3) .... pay you back next week.

Rob: I'm sorry. I (4) .... (not) do it. I've got no money until I get paid next week. You (5) .... have gone to the bank yourself.
Maisie: I suppose, I (6) .... try somebody else. (7) .... you ask Roz for me?
Rob: No, I (8) .... (not). Why me? You (9) .... to do that yourself. You're her friend, not me.
Maisie: Please!
Rob: All right. I'll see what I (10) .... do.

4 Choose the use

Read the sentences below, and choose which use of can *or* could *(A – G) each shows.*

A ability **B** general possibility **C** possibility – specific **D** forbidden (not allowed) **E** request and asking permission **F** giving and refusing permission **G** possible event

Example: Could I borrow your car, please? ☐E☐

1 Children under fourteen can't go in. ☐
2 You can't walk through the park after 10 o'clock. They close the gates then. ☐
3 Can I leave my homework until tomorrow? ☐
4 No, you can't leave your homework until tomorrow night. ☐
5 Could I come shopping with you? ☐
6 I can't start the car. ☐
7 Roz can run a mile in under a minute. ☐
8 Your friend Lucy could have been a supermodel. ☐
9 How fast can a leopard run? ☐
10 Could you visit your sister while you were in Australia? ☐

5 Rewrite the phrases

Rewrite the following phrases using can *or* could.
Example: All credit cards accepted here.
You can use your credit card here.

1 No parking between 8.00 a.m. and 6.00 p.m.
2 The hotel restaurant is open to non-residents.
3 Children under 12 not admitted.
4 No smoking in the air terminal.
5 Foreign currency accepted here.
6 No money refunded for unused tickets.
7 Women only in this room.
8 Choose your own fish from the tank for dinner.
9 No meals served after 10 o'clock.
10 Membership cards for the swimming club accepted for the gym.

FORM

MAY
Positive
I/You/We/He/She/It/They may come
Negative
I/You/We/He/She/It/They may not come
Note:
it is possible to say *mayn't*, but this is not usual.
Question
May I/You/We/He/She/It/They come?
MIGHT
I/You/We/He/She/It/They might come

Negative
I/You/We/He/She/It/They might not come
Note:
It is possible to say *mightn't*, but this is not usual.
Question
Might I/you/we/he/she/it/they come?
Note:
As with all modals, there is no past or future form. We express the past with *may have* or *might have*.
I don't know where he is. He may have gone to the post office.

USE

POSSIBLE EVENTS
1 future
It may/might rain tomorrow.
2 present
He may/might be at work now.
3 past
He may/might have gone to see his aunt.
Note:
Might shows less possibility than *may*.
POLITE REQUESTS OR ASKING PERMISSION
May I have some more tea, please?
May I use your 'phone?
Note
1 It isn't usually used for the second person (you).
2 *Might* is not often used here.

GIVING OR REFUSING PERMISSION
May I use your 'phone?
Yes, you may.
May I go out tonight?
No, you may not.
Note:
Might is not often used here.
WISHING FOR SUCCESS (OR FAILURE*)
May you have a good journey!
May you pass all your exams!
**May he have an accident!*
Notes:
1 We use this more often in written language.
2 *Might* is never used here.
3 *This use for failure is very rare and usually only a joke.

---

1 Write the correct form

Write the correct form of may *or* might.
Example:
She *might* be at the cinema, but I don't think so.

1 She .... come next Wednesday.
2 He .... come with her, but I don't think so.
3 .... the children play in this park?
4 No, they ....(not).
5 Peter .... been here before.
6 I .... seen him last week in town, but I don't think I did.
7 You .... see the Queen when you're in London, but I doubt it.
8 .... you have no troubles in your life!
9 I .... buy the blue car, but I prefer the red one
10 There .... be troubles ahead.

2 Ask for permission

Example:
to go to the cinema tonight
May I go to the cinema tonight?

1 to use the 'phone
2 to borrow your bicycle
3 to go home early
4 to watch television
5 to listen to the radio
6 to have dinner early
7 to borrow your course book
8 to open the window
9 to buy a new pair of shoes
10 to drive the car

3 Choose the use

Read the sentences below, and choose which use of may *or* might *(A–F) each shows.*
A possible future event B possible present event C possible past event D polite request and asking permission E giving or refusing permission F wishing for success (or failure*)

Example:
John may be in the garden. [B]

1 I may see him when I get to Bombay. ☐
2 May we look round the house, please? ☐
3 No, you may not. ☐
4 They might have heard a noise during the night. ☐
5 John might be visiting his sister. ☐
6 Jean might marry Tom, but I doubt it. ☐
7 They might have finished the exam already. ☐
8 May you have all the success you deserve! ☐
9 May the group go into the exhibition now? ☐
10 Yes, they may. ☐

4 Complete the sentences

Complete the sentences with may *or* may have.
Example:
John *may* go to Spain next month

1 Sally .... come here when she was young.
2 They .... be in Istanbul by now.
3 The flowers .... died. We didn't water them.
4 The car is missing. It .... been stolen.
5 That building looks dangerous. It .... fall down.
6 I can't find my watch. Jack .... borrowed it.
7 It .... rain tonight.
8 I .... read that book, but I don't remember much about it.
9 She .... gone away. I haven't seen her for two weeks.
10 They .... borrow some money to buy that business.

5 Complete the dialogue

Complete the dialogue with may *or* might.
Fred: Where are you going for your holiday?
Charlie: I don't know. Although it's too hot for me, I (**1**) .... go to Spain. On the other hand: my holiday's in October, so it (**2**) .... be cooler then.
Fred: Why not go to Malaysia? They rarely appear, but you (**3**) .... see the turtles.
Charlie: (**4**) .... I ask you a question?
Fred: You (**5**) ....
Charlie: Why are you interested in my holiday?
Fred: If you are going to an interesting place, I've got some time free, so I (**6**) .... come with you. I'd like to do that.
Charlie: It's very possible I (**7**) .... not want you.
Fred: Oh, I don't think so. On your own, you (**8**) .... get lonely.
Charlie: I won't.
Fred: (**9**) .... I come with you?
Charlie: No, you (**10**) .... not.
Fred: Oh dear!

6 Write the correct modal

A policeman is talking to Mrs Brown about a burglary in her house. Put MAY *or* MIGHT *in the spaces below. The first two have been done for you.*

Policeman: He *may* have got in through the window. It was open.
Mrs Brown: But you can't open it any more.
Policeman: It's unlikely, but he *might* have a door-key.
Mrs Brown: A door-key! Why do you think that? Do you think it (**1**) .... be a member of the family. I doubt that.
Policeman: It's unlikely, but it (**2**) .... be one of your children.
Mrs Brown: My son or daughter. Do you think it's possible they (**3**) .... have done this.
Policeman: Yes. They (**4**) .... have needed some money.
Mrs Brown: I (**5**) .... be a careful parent; but I will always help them.
Policeman: (**6**) .... I look at the broken desk again?
Mrs Brown: Yes, of course. I suppose there (**7**) .... be a clue there.
Policeman: It is likely that I (**8**) .... have to take fingerprints.
Mrs Brown: From the family? So any one of us (**9**) .... be guilty. That's unlikely.
Policeman: We can't be too careful. (**10**) .... I go into the study again?
Mrs Brown: All right. But (**11**) .... I come with you?
Policeman: Of course. But it (**12**) .... upset you.
Mrs Brown: I don't think so.

UNIT 15 Modals 4: Offers, Permission and Requests
Can I go out — Yes, you can

USE

Can, could, may, and might sometimes have almost the same use.
REQUESTS
Can I have another cup of tea, please?
Could I have another cup of tea, please?
May I have another cup of tea, please?
Note:
Might is not often used here.
We also make requests of other people.
Can you help me, please?
Could you buy me some stamps at the post office?
Note:
May and might are not used for requests for the second person.
ASKING PERMISSION
Can I use the phone, please?
Could I use the phone, please?
May I use the phone, please?
Note:
Might is not often used here.
GIVING PERMISSION
Can I go out tonight?   Yes, you can.
Could I go out tonight?   Yes, you can.
May I go out tonight?   Yes, you may.
Notes:
1 Could is not used to give permission.
2 Might is not often used here.
REFUSING PERMISSION AND REQUESTS
Can I use your 'phone?   No, you can't.
Could I use your 'phone?   No, you can't.

May I use your 'phone?   No, you may not.
Can you help me?   No, I can't.
Could you buy me some   No, I can't. I'm not
stamps   going to the post
                               office.

Note:
Could and might are not used to refuse permission or requests.
OFFERS
Can/Could/May I help you?
Note:
Might is not often used here.
For offers, permission and requests:
Can is the most used form.
Could is more polite.
May is the most polite.
POSSIBLE EVENTS
1 present
She could/may/might be at work now.
2 future
It could/may/might rain tomorrow.
3 past
They could/may/might have already seen the film.
Note: We do not use can here.
For possible events:
Could is the most possible.
May is less possible.
Might is the least possible.

---

1 Write *can*, *could*, *may* or *might*

Example:
He *could* be at home by now. (most possible)

1 .... I drive your car? (more polite)
2 Could you lend me £100? No, I ....(most used form)
3 They .... have bought the meat for tomorrow's dinner. (least possible)
4 That .... be the answer. (less possible)
5 We .... be in Spain tomorrow. (most possible)
6 I .... win the $40,000 prize. (least possible)
7 They .... have already finished. (less possible)
8 .... I stay here tonight? (most used form)
9 Cheer up! We .... win the match! (less possible)
10 The man at the end of the street .... have taken the money. (most possible)

2 Ask for permission

Example:
to stay home from school today (most polite)
May I stay home from school today?

1 to go to the cinema (most used form)
2 to use the computer (most polite)
3 to go home early (most polite)
4 to see your birthday present (more polite)
5 to have a party next week (most polite)
6 to go on a ski-trip to the mountains (most used form)
7 to go swimming (more polite)
8 to close the door (most polite)
9 to have a day's holiday on Thursday (most used form)
10 to drive the car (most polite)

USE

MUSTN'T
We use *mustn't* for laws and rules
You mustn't steal.
You mustn't drink and drive.
CAN'T
We use *can't*, when we don't have permission to do something. The permission is given by someone who is not a law person, e.g. parent, teacher, boss, etc.
1   *Can I go out tonight?*
    No, you can't.
2   *I can't go out tonight.*

Note:

We sometimes use *may not* instead of *can't*
In example 1 if the person asking uses *may*
May I go out tonight?
No, you may not!
This is a very strong form.
MUSTN'T and CAN'T
We can use either *mustn't* or *can't*
1   when the law or rule is not criminal
You can't/mustn't park here.
2   when the rule is refusing permission
You can't/mustn't wear heavy shoes in the hostel.

---

1   Complete the sentences

Complete the sentences with mustn't *or* can't. *Use the letters below to help you.*
A for laws and rules
B when we don't have permission to do something
C when the law or rule is not criminal, or the rule is refusing permission
Example:
You *mustn't* steal. (A)

1   No, you .... stay late.   (B)
2   You .... go on a train without buying
    a ticket.   (C)
3   You .... walk on the grass.   (C)
4   You .... drive my car.   (B)
5   You .... be late for the concert.
    They won't let you in.   (A)
6   You .... swim in this river.   (C)
7   You .... drive at more that 110 kph.   (A)
8   You .... touch the pictures in the
    museum.   (A)
9   You .... stay at home. You must go
    to school.   (B)
10 You .... climb over the wall into
    that garden.   (B)

2   Write the use

*Look at the sentences below and write the use. Then put a cross (**X**) where you can change* can't *to* mustn't.
Examples:
You can't play tennis at
the weekend. *refusing permission* ☐
You can't park here. *a rule* X

1   No, you can't go to the disco tonight.
    ....   ☐
2   You can't leave before you see
    the boss. ....   ☐
3   You can't pick those flowers.
    ....   ☐
4   You can't have my exercise book
    tonight. ....   ☐
5   You can't swim in this river.
    ....   ☐
6   You can't feed the animals in
    the park. ....   ☐
7   No, you can't stay here all night.
    ....   ☐
8   You can't telephone him after ten
    o'clock at night. ....   ☐
9   No, you can't invite her to your party.
    ....   ☐
10 You can't sit there. It's the
    boss's chair. ....   ☐

3   Rewrite these rules

Example:
No parking here.
You can't/mustn't park here.

1   No smoking in this restaurant.
2   No drinking after 11 p. m. in here.
3   No children under fourteen allowed.
4   No guns.
5   No admission after 5.45.
6   Don't drink and drive.
7   Don't get on the train without a ticket.
8   Don't stand too close to the paintings.

FORM

SHOULD
Positive
I/You/We/He/She/It/They should go
Negative
I/You/We/He/She/It/They should not go/shouldn't go
Note:
We usually use the short form, *shouldn't*.
Question
Should I/You/We/He/She/It/They go?
Note:
The past form is *should have*.
He should have gone.

OUGHT TO
Positive
I/You/We/He/She/It/They ought to go
Negative
I/You/We/He/She/It/They ought not to go
Note:
We usually use the short form, *oughtn't to*.
Question
Ought I/You/We/He/She/It/They to go
Note:
1 With question words – *when, where, why, what, who, how, how often* – we rarely use *ought to*.
2 The past form is *ought to have*.
She ought to have gone.

USE

WHAT IT IS IMPORTANT TO DO
I should do my homework tonight.
You ought to get that book tomorrow. It's important for the exam.
I should have done my homework last night. (past)
You ought to have got that book yesterday. It's important for the exam. (past)
WHAT IT IS BETTER TO DO
There should be more people on this committee.
I ought to get more money for this work.
There should have been more people on this committee. (past)
I ought to have got more money for this work. (past)
GIVING ADVICE OR OPINIONS
If you feel ill, you should see the doctor.

If you can't see the blackboard, you ought to move to the front of the class.

SOMETHING THAT WILL PROBABLY HAPPEN OR IS EXPECTED TO HAPPEN
The train gets in at quarter past twelve, so Tony should be here by one, o'clock.
The train gets in at one, so Tony shouldn't be here before two o'clock.
Note:
We usually use *should* for this use.
SOMETHING THAT IS EXPECTED TO HAVE HAPPENED, BUT MAY NOT
The train got in at quarter past twelve, so Tony should have been here by one o'clock (but he hasn't arrived yet).
The train came in late, so Tony shouldn't have been here until after one (but he's already arrived).

---

1   **Complete the sentences**

Complete the sentences with should *or* ought.
Example:
You .... start work before nine.
You should start work before nine.
They .... (not) to throw stones at the animals.
They ought not to throw stones at the animals.

1 He .... be finished by now.
2 They .... to catch the earlier train.
3 .... you do that?
4 We .... (not) swim in the river. It's dangerous!

5 .... you to speak to her like that? It was very rude.
6 They .... (not) to play in the park so late at night.
7 Those clothes .... be cheaper. They're much too expensive.
8 They .... have told you they weren't coming.
9 He's a very good footballer. He .... play for a top team.
10 I .... to tell him; but I don't want to.
11 She .... be here by now. It's already 9 o'clock.
12 You .... (not) spend so much money on shoes. You never wear them!

2 Make questions

Example:
Yes, they should pay him more money.
Should they pay him more money?
They ought to send him to Turkey. (Where)
Where ought they to send him?

1 Yes, they should clean their car more often.
2 They should be here at midday. (When)
3 Yes, he ought to telephone her.
4 The students should do their homework every night. (How often)
5 Students should hand in their work at the beginning of the lesson. (When)
6 No, he ought not to work so hard.
7 Yes, they ought to spend so much money on their child.
8 They should finish the work this afternoon. (When)
9 No, he shouldn't have spoken to her like that.
10 Yes, they ought to have finished by now.
11 She should go to the hospital once a month (How often)
12 He ought not to go out every lunch-time.

3 Choose the use

Read the sentences below, and choose which use of should or ought to (A–E) each shows.
A What it is important to do
B What is better to do
C Giving advice or opinion
D Something that will probably happen or is expected to happen
E Something that is expected to have happened, but may not
Example: They should have finished by now E

1 You ought to go to the dentist if your tooth aches.
2 There should be more taxis in this town.
3 She should pass all her exams.
4 This computer should last for at least five years.
5 You shouldn't eat so much.
6 That bell ought to be quieter.
7 You should put the light on. It's too dark in here.
8 I should have told her not to go.
9 You should always read notices carefully.
10 You shouldn't swim there. It's dangerous.
11 They should have checked the timetable.

They've missed the train.
12 He should find all his money.

4 Complete the dialogue

Alan and Jane are discussing the interview he has had for a new job. Complete the dialogue by adding should or ought to. The first one has been done for you.

Jane: They *should* have given you more information about the job conditions.
Alan: I know, but I (1) .... have asked for more.
Jane: You (2) .... 'phone them now.
Alan: Why (3) .... I?
Jane: You need more information.
Alan: They haven't given me the job yet.
Jane: But you (4) .... to show some interest.
Alan: I (5) .... have done that at the interview.
Jane: You (6) .... to 'phone them.
Alan: No, not now. I (7) .... just wait until they write.
Jane: You (8) .... have received some written details about the job.
Alan: A lot of things (9) .... have been done. They weren't.
Jane: But you (10) .... do something. You (11) .... (not) just sit there.
Alan: There's nothing I can do. I think I (12) .... just relax.

5

Write should or should have using the verb in brackets.

EXAMPLE:
I (be) stronger yesterday.
I should have been stronger yesterday.
No, but you (be) more careful next time.
No, but you should be more careful next time.

1 (tell) I him what I've done?
2 Yes. You (not lie) to him yesterday.
3 I know. I (be) honest. But it's very difficult.
4 You (always tell) the truth. Now look at the problems we're having.
5 Yes. I see that now. We (not take) the money from Mother.
6 We (ask) for some when we needed it.
7 Mother (not be) so mean all the time.
8 We (not want) to buy so many new clothes.
9 Yes, we (buy) new clothes.
10 You're right. We (always look) smart.

Short Responses

So am I; Nor / Neither does she

FORM AND USE

We use these short responses to show that the situation is the same for someone or something else.

SO

We use *so* when responding to a positive statement. We make our responses by putting *so* at the beginning of the response followed by

1 an auxiliary and then the subject

I like New York. (present simple)

So does my uncle. (present simple auxiliary)

The old Jaguar used a lot of petrol. (past simple)

So did the old Mercedes-Benz. (past simple auxiliary)

So + auxiliary (in the same tense) *+ subject.*

2 a modal and then the subject

I can swim two miles.

So can I.

So + modal + subject

NOR/NEITHER

We use *nor/neither* when responding to a negative statement. Although the verb in the main statement is negative, in the response with *neither* or *nor* the auxiliary is positive.

I don't like travelling by train.

Nor does my aunt/Neither does my aunt.

Sheila has never been to Sweden.

Nor have I!/Neither have I.

I can't speak Japanese.

Nor can Daisy.

Neither/nor + auxiliary/modal (positive) *+ subject*

---

1 Match the sentences

Match the sentences and the short answers. The first one has been done for you.

1 John gets home late on Fridays.
2 I haven't seen that film yet.
3 David'll go to Rome for his holiday.
4 I can run a mile in four minutes.
5 Mary has got a new job.
6 John didn't go to the party.
7 Mary isn't very clever.
8 I'd like to go to Chile.
9 My football team lost today.
10 George is going to Hungary next week.
11 Tim can't drive.

a) So can John.
b) So has Kate.
c) So would I.
d) Nor can Thelma.
e) So will Jane.
f) Nor have I.
g) So did mine.
h) So does Alec.
i) So is John.
j) Nor did Ruth.
k) Nor is Mick.

---

2 Complete the responses in brackets.

Example:

Mick's leaving his job next week. (so/Dave)

So is Dave.

1 They won't be able to see the film. (neither/we)
2 I don't like that picture. (nor/I)
3 The flowers in his garden are beautiful. (so/those in Mary's garden)
4 Saudi Arabia exports a lot of oil. (so/Iran)
5 Mexico City is very big. (so/Tokyo)
6 John can fly on his own now. (so/Kate)
7 I wouldn't like to go to that school. (nor/I)
8 I watched television last night. (so/I)
9 They didn't know about the accident. (nor/we)
10 I've spent a lot of money today. (so/I)
11 I've got a very small flat. (so/they)
12 She hasn't seen that film. (nor/we)
13 I work on Saturdays. (so/I)
14 We want to visit Hong Kong soon. (so/she)
15 John can't find the sort of car he really wants. (neither/we)
16 Maria is very rich. (so/Anne)
17 I can be there at 7 o'clock tomorrow. (so/I)
18 I haven't been to college yet. (nor/he)
19 She didn't like Tom very much. (neither/we)
20 He leaves early on Friday. (so/I)

3 Complete the responses

Complete the responses by writing so *or* neither *at the beginning of each.*

Example:
John wasn't pleased with the result. *Neither* was Rosie.
David can come. *So* can Mary.

1 Paul didn't know the answer. .... did Mary.
2 South Africa is a very beautiful country. .... is New Zealand.
3 Tigers can be dangerous. .... can lions.
4 I don't enjoy going to the circus. .... do I.
5 Mary's got a very important job. .... has her husband.
6 I wouldn't like to be famous. .... would I.
7 She'll be fourteen soon. .... will he.
8 We haven't been to the disco for a long time. .... have we.
9 I couldn't get any tickets for the tennis match. .... could I.
10 The Turkish team arrives ten tomorrow. .... does the Moroccan team.
11 I haven't seen him for ages. .... have I.
12 We can't afford to live there .... can we.
13 I really like Andrew. .... do I.
14 I can't cook very well. .... can Janet.
15 They haven't been here very long. .... has she.

4 Write the correct responses

Here is some information about four countries. Write the correct responses to the statements below.

Brazil	Britain	Spain	Sri Lanka
mid-continent	island	mid-continent	island
South America	Europe	Europe	Asia
115m people	60m people	37m people	16m people
rich	rich	rich	poor
8m sq. km	244k sq. km	504k sq. km.	65k. sq. km.
Republic	Monarchy	Monarchy	Republic

Example:
Brazil is a mid-continental country. So *is Spain.*

1 Britain is an island.
   So ....
2 Sri Lanka isn't in Europe.
   Nor ....
3 Spain has fewer than 50m people.
   So ....
4 Britain isn't as large as Spain.
   Nor ....
5 Britain has a bigger population than Spain.
   So ....
6 Brazil and Spain are rich countries.
   So ....
7 Spain isn't an island.
   Nor ....
8 Sri Lanka and Britain are smaller than Brazil.
   So ....
9 Spain isn't a republic.
   Nor ....
10 Sri Lanka has got a President.
   So ....

5 Complete the dialogue

Alan and Bob are talking about a film and a concert. Complete the dialogue, by giving the correct response. The first one has been done for you.

Alan: I was at the cinema last night.
Bob: That's funny. *So was I.* I didn't see you.
Alan: I was upstairs.
Bob: So (1) ....
Alan: I didn't like the film.
Bob: Nor (2) .... But I like the actor who was in it.
Alan: Oh, so (3) .... He's very good.
Bob: Did you see his last film? I didn't.
Alan: Nor (4) .... I didn't like the story.
Bob: No, nor (5) .... Have you got tickets for that pop concert next week? I have.
Alan: Yes, so (6) .... I'm going with Jane.
Bob: So (7) .... So you can't be. I've bought two tickets. One for me and one for her.
Alan: So (8) .... And mine cost £20 each.
Bob: So (9) .... I always go to concerts with her.
Alan: So (10) ....
Bob: Are you sure?

Conditional 1

If you come, I'll meet you; If I'm in London, I go to the theatre

FORM AND USE

If + present simple, *will* + base verb
We use this form for a definite plan for the future, but something is uncertain.
If you come *on the 4.15 train,* I'll meet *you.*
Here the verb in the main clause is in the future – *I'll meet you*, and the verb after *if* is in the present simple tense. <u>We are talking about a possible event in the future.</u> The speaker intends to meet the person, but it is not certain that the person will come on the **4.15** train.

If + present simple, present simple
We use this form for a usual event
If *I'm in London, I go to the theatre.*
Here the verbs in both clauses are in the present tense. We are talking about something the person always does when he/she is in London.

Order of clauses
You can make the *if* clause the first or second clause in the sentence.
If you come on the 4.15 train, I'll meet you.
or
I'll meet you if you come on the 4.15 train.
The clause which comes first is the one that is more important for the speaker.
Note:
Only use a comma between the clauses, when the *if* clause is the first one.

Negative use
1 We can also make negative conditions about things that might not happen.
I **won't see** *the new play if I go to Germany in January.*
The speaker isn't certain about visiting Germany. She is looking at things she won't be able to do, if she goes to Germany. She might also say:
I'll see the new play if I **don't go** *to Germany in January.*
You can have a negative in both parts of the sentence.
You **won't see** *the football championship match, if you* **don't get** *your tickets soon.*
2 When we are talking about things that usually happen.
If he **isn't** *on holiday, he always attends the committee meeting.*
If + present simple (negative), present simple
3 When we are talking about things that usually don't happen.
Robert doesn't visit *his old school if he's in Istanbul.*
If + present simple, present simple (negative)
Note:
Notice the different part of the sentence for the negative in 2 and 3.

---

1 **Match the parts**

Match the parts of the sentence below. The first one has been done for you.

1 You'll be late
2 They won't let you in
3 Rob will be angry
4 He'll enjoy that book
5 They won't pass the exam
6 He'll have an accident
7 They'll get lost
8 She'll leave her job
9 You'll have a good holiday
10 You'll win a lot of money
11 I'll help you

a) if he doesn't drive more slowly.
b) if you buy a lottery ticket.
c) if they don't work harder.
d) if you go to Bodrum on the Turkish coast.
e) if you don't hurry.
f) if you break his glass dish.
g) if you want me to.
h) if you don't give them a map.
i) if you arrive late.
j) if he likes comic novels.
k) if they don't give her more money.

2 **Complete these sentences**

Complete the sentences by writing the verbs in the correct tense.
Example:
If I (see) him, I (tell) him.

If I see him, I'll tell him.
1 Mary (not like) it if you (come) late.
2 If they (pass) the exam, they (have) a big party.
3 They (lose) if they (not get) better players.
4 I (help) her if she (want) me to.
5 That hotel (be) cheaper if you (go) in March.

32

7 If you (go) to Sydney at Christmas, it (be) very hot.
8 They (sell) the business if they (get) more customers.
9 If you (dress) well, they (give) you the job.
10 You (have) an interview if you (apply) before next week.

3 Choose the use

Read the sentences below, and choose which use of this conditional form (A or B) each shows.
A A definite plan, with something uncertain
B A usual event
Examples:
If I meet him, we have a meal in a good restaurant. $\boxed{B}$
If I meet him, I'll invite him to dinner. $\boxed{A}$

1 If he comes home late, he brings his wife flowers. ☐
2 If he goes to Rome, he'll see the Colosseum. ☐
3 If you go by coach, you'll see better country than if you go by train. ☐
4 If you work hard, you pass exams. ☐
5 If they make all that noise, the neighbours will complain. ☐
6 If the neighbours complain, the police will come. ☐
7 You get good treatment if you go to that doctor. ☐
8 You'll lose all your money if you invest in that company. ☐
9 If he brings his wife flowers, she wants to know the reason. ☐
10 I'll be very lucky if I win the marathon. ☐

4 Write the correct tense

Write the verbs in the correct tense. The use, A (definite plan) or B (usual event), is given to help you.
Examples:
If she (go) to Rome, she (stay) at the Astoria Hotel. (B)
If she goes to Rome, she stays at the Astoria Hotel.
If she (go) to Rome, she (be able) to visit the Forum. (A)
If she goes to Rome, she'll be able to visit the Forum.

1 If I (lend) him the money, he (be able) to have a holiday. (A)
2 If I (watch) television late at night, I (fall) asleep. (B)
3 If they (have) a party, all the neighbours (get) angry. (B)
4 The boss (be) angry if you (leave) early today. (A)

5 You (arrive) too early if you (take) the 9 o'clock train. (A)
6 If you (arrive) early, you (have to) wait outside. (B)
7 If you (finish) the work on time, I (take) you to a good restaurant. (A)
8 If it (be) hot, they (go) to their house by the sea. (B)
9 If it (rain), I (not go) to the tennis match today. (A)
10 If it (rain), they (cancel) the game. (B)

5 Answer the questions

Answer the questions with the information given.
Examples:
What'll you do, if you win £1 million? (buy/large house)
I'll buy a large house.
What do you do, if the TV breaks down? (go/bed)
I go to bed.

1 What does he do if he goes to London? (see/Queen)
2 What'll they do if they lose the game? (be/miserable)
3 What'll you do if they're late? (go/party alone)
4 What'll you do if you get the job? (buy/new car)
5 What'll she do if he gets the job? (marry/him)
6 What do you do if you miss the train? (take/bus)
7 What'll you do if it rains tomorrow? (stay/home)
8 What'll you do if the sun shines? (swim/the lake)
9 What'll she do if she loses her job? (have/holiday)
10 What do you do if the car breaks down? (call/garage)
11 What does Jane do if the students are late? (is angry)
12 What'll you do if they cancel the concert? (go/cinema)
13 What do you do if there are no buses? (go/train)
14 What'll Andrew do if he can't sell his house? (stay/Italy)
15 What do you do if the fire-alarm rings? (run/fire escape)

Think of five other questions to ask your friends.

UNIT 20 Conditional 2
If you came, I'd meet you
FORM AND USE

If + the past simple, *would* + base verb
We use this form for something in the future which is possible, but unlikely.
*If she **loved** him, **she'd marry** him.*
Here in the main clause, there is *would* + base verb – *she'd marry him* – and the verb after *if* is in the past simple tense.
Note:
With this conditional form, we often say: *If I were . . .* not *If I was . . .*
If I were you, I'd finish that work today.
If + past simple, past simple
We use this form when the speaker is talking abut something he/she always did the past.
If I went to London, I always went to the theatre.
Here the speaker is talking about every time he went to London in the past – *always went to the theatre.* We use the past simple in both clauses.
Order of clauses
You can make the *if* clause the first or second clause in the sentence.

If she loved him, she'd marry him.
or
She'd marry him if she loved him.
The clause which comes first is the more important for the speaker.
Note:
You only put a comma between the clause when the *if* clause comes first.
Negative use
1 When we are talking about an unlikely future event.
*I **wouldn't know** Tim, if I saw him.*
Here the speaker doesn't expect to meet Tim and is admitting that he wouldn't recognize him.
would + (negative) + base verb, *if* + past simple
2 When we are talking about regular events
*If I **didn't go** to London, I **wouldn't see** my sister.*
Here the speaker is explaining why he goes to London. It is the only time he can see his sister. In other words, when he goes to London, he sees his sister. There is a negative in both parts of the sentence.
If + past simple (negative), *would* (negative) + base verb.

---

1 Match the parts

Match the parts of the sentences below. The first one has been done for you.

1 If you came on Wednesday
2 If John worked harder
3 If Alan played better
4 If you wrote a popular book
5 If you listened to the news
6 If Mary saved more money
7 If David lived in the country
8 If Sam loved Lydia
9 If he married her
10 If he was rich
11 If he had a big house

a) she'd be able to have a good holiday.
b) he'd have lots of parties.
c) he'd be very rich.
d) he'd buy a big house.
e) he would be promoted.
f) I would meet you.
g) you'd know about the 'plane crash.
h) he would be in the team.
i) you'd be very famous.
j) he'd marry her.
k) he'd have to have a car.

2 Complete the sentences

Complete the sentence writing the verbs in the correct tense.
Example:
If I (see) him, I (tell) him.
If I saw him, I'd tell him.

1 Jack (not like) it if you (do) better than him in the exam.

2 If you (pass) the exam, you (be) the youngest person in the top class.
3 If you (fail) the exam, you (be able) to take it again next year.
4 I (buy) a house by the sea if I (live) in Greece.
5 If you (buy) a house by the sea, you (have) lots of problems.
6 The house (be) in danger if there (be) a bad storm.
7 I (not live) by the sea if you (pay) me £2 million.
8 They (be) very happy if he (play) in the concert.

34

9 If they (tell) people about him, a lot of people (come) to the concert.

10 If a lot of people (come) to the concert, they (get) a lot of money.

3 **Choose the use**

Read the sentences below, and choose which use of this conditional form (A or B) each shows.
A Something that is possible, but unlikely
B A usual event in the past
Examples:
If he came to work early in the morning, he left early in the evening. [B]
If they lived in Turkey, they'd have better weather. [A]

1 If I went into that café, I'd meet my neighbours. ☐
2 I'd go to Crow's restaurant if I wanted a good meal. ☐
3 If the news was all about war, I switched off the television. ☐
4 If Charlie was nice, you knew he wanted something from you. ☐
5 If the flag was raised, the President was at home. ☐
6 You had to stay behind at the end of the day if you got bad marks at school. ☐
7 He felt much better if he went to the gym each day. ☐
8 If I found a nice holiday place, I'd go there every year. ☐
9 He'd be happier if he went out with his friends more often. ☐
10 If you read that book, you'd learn a lot about space travel. ☐

4 **Write the correct tense**

Write the verbs in the correct tense. The use, A (possible but unlikely) or B (a usual event in the past), is given to help you.
Example:
You (get) a better hotel if you (pay) more money. (A)
You'd get a better hotel if you paid more money.

1 If they (go) away for a long holiday, they (give) their cat to the neighbours. (B)
2 If the television (break), they (not know) what to do in the evening. (A)
3 If she (go) to the Maldives, she (have) a good holiday. (A)
4 If you (eat) at that restaurant, it (be) expensive. (B)

5 The journey (take) a long time if you (travel) by coach. (A)
6 If I (be) you, I (buy) another car. (A)
7 If it (rain), she (not go) to work. (B)
8 If it (be) sunny, she (play) tennis all day. (B)
9 If you (go) to the moon, you (have to) wear special heavy boots. (A)
10 If you (buy) that expensive chair, you (not have) any money for other furniture. (A)

5 **Answer the questions**

Answer the questions with the information given.
Example:
What would you do if you won a lot of money? (have/long holiday)
I'd have a long holiday.
What did you do if you missed the last bus? (get/taxi)
I got a taxi

1 What would she do if she was poor? (marry/rich man)
2 What did they do if they failed their exams? (be/very miserable)
3 What would she do if her boy-friend left her? (find/new boy-friend)
4 What did you do if the river flooded your house? (call/rescue service)
5 What would he do if he lost all his money? (have to work)
6 What did you do if you didn't have a car? (walk to work)
7 What would you do if you lived in another country? (learn/the language)
8 What would you do if you were a famous film star? (have/a big house in Hollywood)
9 What would you do if you had a spaceship? (go/Mars)
10 What did you do if the parties were too loud? (call/the police)

Think of five other questions to ask your friends.

The Passive
The house was built in 1897

FORM

THE PASSIVE

1 Look at this sentence:
Bell invented the telephone.
This sentence is called an **active** sentence. The order of the sentence is

SUBJECT	VERB	OBJECT
Bell	*invented*	*the telephone*

2 We can say the same thing in another way with a **passive** sentence.
The telephone was invented by Bell.
Now we have changed the order.

SUBJECT	VERB	AGENT
The telephone	*was invented*	*by Bell*

When we make the passive, we use the correct form of the verb *to be* + the past participle:
*I **am loved** by everyone.* (present simple)
*The building **was completed** in 1637.* (past simple)
*They **have been paid** already.* (present perfect)
*We **will be taken** on trips.* (future)
In the passive, the object of the active sentence becomes the subject, and the subject of the active sentence becomes the agent. The agent is the person/people or thing that does the action.
David bought the last pen in the shop. (active)
The last pen in the shop was bought by David. (passive)
Notes:
1 Some verbs like *give* can have two objects
Mary gave me that book.
In the passive we can say either
I was given that book by Mary
or
That book was given to me by Mary.
2 Only verbs that usually have an object can have a passive form.
3 We also use modal verbs with passive.
If the action is in the present or future, the form is Modal + *be* + past participle.
*John has worked hard this term, he **must be given** a prize*
*The company has no money, I **may not be paid** this month.*
If the action is in the past, then the form is Modal + *have been* + past participle.
He's just bought a big house. He must have been given a lot of money.

USE

1 To focus on what we are talking about
When we say *Bell invented the telephone*, we are talking about Bell.
When we say *The telephone was invented by Bell*, we are talking about the telephone.
2 To focus on the action but not the person
Ten goals were scored.
Here we are not interested in which member of the football team scored the goals. Our interest is the number of goals.

3 When we don't know the agent
They built that house in 1897.
Here we don't know who built the house. The best passive form is
That house was built in 1897.
Note:
We also do not use the agent when it is understood who or what did the action.
Mrs Bold put the plates in the sink. When the washing up was done (by Mrs Bold), *she went to make the beds.*

---

1 **Write the correct form**

Write the correct passive form of the verb.
Example:
Everything must (sell) by 5th July.
Everything must be sold by 5th July.

1 No coats may (leave) here.
2 No children (allow) to see this film.
3 All these paintings (do) by the artist when he was a young man.
4 All our goods (check) by our sales staff.
5 Our staff (train) to help you.
6 Tickets for the football match must (collect) by Friday at midday.
7 The work should (finish) by tomorrow.
8 The exam results will (send) to your school in September.
9 At this school, all children (teach) English.
10 All the offices (clean) every day before eight o'clock.

2 Make the sentences passive

Example:
David drove the car.
The car was driven by David.

1 Jane cooked the dinner.
2 Robin wrote that book.
3 I made that table.
4 Alan will win the marathon.
5 They built the road in 1987.
6 They planted those trees in 1915.
7 John gave Mary that expensive diamond ring.
8 They stole the television and video last week.
9 They first climbed Mt Everest in 1953.
10 Peter bought the last cake in the shop.

3 Choose the correct form

Choose the correct form of the verb, active or passive, and underline it.
Example:
English (spoke/is spoken) in many countries.

1 The accident (see/was seen) by a lot of people, but nobody (talked/was talked) to the police about it.
2 Ford (have made/have been made) cars for eighty years and now their cars (sell/are sold) all over the world.
3 The thief (didn't see/wasn't seen) by anyone, although he (took/was taken) the jewels in a crowded room.
4 The letter (posted/was posted) on 1st March, but it (didn't deliver/wasn't delivered) until 23rd April.
5 The package (contained/was contained) a lot of money, but (lost/was lost) in the post.
6 That car (owns/is owned) by a racing driver, who always (drives/is driven) it very fast.
7 That film (made/was made) in India, but the story (wrote/was written) by a Frenchman.
8 I always (travel/am travelled) first class. You (give/are given) much better food.
9 The lights (put/were put) out when the family (heard/was heard) the burglar.
10 He didn't like the present that he (gave/was given) for his birthday, so he (sold/was sold) it.

4 Write sentences

Write sentences with the underlined words as the focus. The sentences may be active or passive. Be careful! Choose the right tense!
Example:
The car / sell / for £12,000 yesterday.
The car was sold for £12,000 yesterday.
English / teach / Mr Brown next year.
Mr Brown will teach English next year.

1 Robert / take / the photographs of the wedding / last week.
2 Daisy / paint / her house / next month.
3 His parents / allow / that boy / to stay up late.
4 You / mustn't / play / games / in this park.
5 My father / make / that table / ten years ago.
6 Italy / win / the World Cup / in 1982.
7 Fire / destroy / that building / last month.
8 One man / can / do / this work.
9 Richard / catch / the thief when he was shopping in the High Street.
10 A boy / break / the window / this morning.

In which two sentences could the agent be omitted?

5 Complete the dialogue

David and Jane are talking about a painting David has done. Complete the dialogue with the passive form for the verb.

David: I may (**1** give) a prize for this.
Jane: For that! It looks as if it (**2** paint) in five minutes.
David: Five minutes! It (**3** do) very slowly and carefully.
Jane: (**4** show) it at the exhibition last month?
David: No. But it (**5** see) by thousands of people in the future.
Jane: And where will it (**6** hang)?
David: In the National Gallery. And it (**7** light) with a special light.
Jane: (**8** buy) it by the gallery?
David: Not yet. It must (**9** see) by the head of the gallery first. But it doesn't matter. It (**10** sell) already. My mother's bought it.

Reported Speech 1: Statements (What People Say or Tell You to Do)
John said he was painting the house

FORM

REPORTED STATEMENTS
Look at this sentence:
'I'm painting the house,' said John.
Now look at this sentence and notice the changes:
*Charles spoke to Alan. John said **he was** painting the house.*
When Charles reported to Alan what John said, the pronoun *I* became *he* and *am* (present) became *was* (past).
We sometimes put *that* after *said*; but it isn't necessary
'John said (that) he was painting the house.'

Verb changes
When we report what someone has said, we usually make the following verb changes:
1 Present simple to past simple
I come here every week.' → *She said she came here every week.*
2 Present continuous to past continuous
'I'm painting the house.' → *He said he was painting the house.*
3 Past simple or present perfect to past perfect (*see* Note below).
'I bought some new chairs in the sale' → *She said she had bought some new chairs in the sale.*
'I've seen that film twice.' → *He said he had seen that film twice.*
4 *am/is/are going to* become *was/were going to*
'We're going to meet in Paris' → *She said they were going to meet in Paris.*
5 *will* becomes *would*
'I'll come early' → *He said he would come early.*
6 *can* becomes *could*
'I can do all the exercises.' → *She said she could do all the exercises.*
Note:
We only use the past perfect on special occasions,

such as here with reported statements and also with reported questions. It is formed with the simple past of *have* (*had*) + past participle:
Simple past = *I went*, past perfect = *I had gone*.
You will find its other uses and be able to practise this tense in Book 3 (Intermediate).**Pronoun changes**
We also make changes with the pronouns, but this depends on who the reporting speaker is.
'I like playing netball, Peter,' Joan said.
1 *I told Peter I liked playing netball.*
Here the pronoun *I* remains the same, because the reporting speaker is Joan – the same speaker.
2 *Joan told Peter **she** liked playing netball.*
Here we change the pronoun *I* to *she*, because there is a different reporting speaker.
Note:
Be careful with the pronoun change!
Reporting verbs: *say* and *tell*
1 We can use *tell* instead of *say*, but when we use *tell*, we want to know who the speaker told.
*David **told me** he was painting his house.*
*Mary **told Frank** she could do all the exercises.*
Note:
We always tell **someone** something.
2 We use *tell* + the infinitive form to report orders.
'Close the door, please, John.'
He **told** John **to close** the door.
When it is negative, we put *not* before the infinitive.
'Don't run so fast, Kate.'
She **told** Kate **not to run** so fast.

---

1 Match the statements

Match the reported statements with the original statements. The first one has been done for you.

1 They said they were going to the King's Hotel.
2 They said they could come next week.
3 He said he wouldn't be able to see the doctor.
4 She said she was writing the essay.
5 They said they hadn't been to the concert.
6 He said there wasn't any milk in the shop.
7 She said she'd posted the letters.
8 She said she didn't play the piano very well.
9 She told them to open their books at page 12.
10 He said the fire had destroyed the factory.
11 She told Peter to give the dog some food.

a) 'There isn't any milk in the shop.'
b) 'Open your books at page 12.'
c) 'Give the dog some food, Peter.'
d) 'I won't be able to see the doctor.'
e) 'We're going to the King's Hotel.'
f) 'We can come next week.'
g) 'I don't play the piano very well.'
h) 'I'm writing the essay.'
i) 'The fire destroyed the factory.'
j) 'I've posted the letters.'
k) 'We haven't been to the concert.'

2 Write reported statements

Write reported statements for the following sentences. The name in brackets is the person who made the statement.

Example:

'I'm staying at home all the week.' (Jane)

Jane said she was staying at home all the week.

1 'My brother is living in Istanbul.' (David)
2 'David can't get a ticket for the concert.' (Mary)
3 'The bell doesn't work.' (Sam)
4 'Don't break that chair, Fred!' (He)
5 'Bring me that book, Alan!' (Rosie)
6 'I'll be in London then.' (Daisy)
7 'The train's late.' (Harry)
8 'I'm going to visit my mother in August.' (Jill)
9 'We want to see the play at the local theatre.' (Alec and Dan)
10 'I'm too old to play football in the park.' (Ken)

3 Write the original statements

Write the original statements for these reported statements.

Example:

He said he was going to see his brother.

'I'm going to see my brother.'

1 She said she didn't like tomatoes.
2 They said they were buying the house at the corner of the street.
3 He said he wouldn't be here during January.
4 She said the flowers were beautiful.
5 They said the football team played badly.
6 He said he couldn't come.
7 She said she hadn't been to Italy since 1995.
8 He said he didn't watch television.
9 She said she'd lost all her money on the train.
10 They said they always listened to the news at eight o'clock.

4 Write reported statements

Write reported statements for the following sentences using say *or* tell. *The name in brackets is the person who made the statement.*

Example:

'I'm going out.' (Fred/say)

Fred said he was going out.

'I want to watch television, Peter.' (Jane/tell)

Jane told Peter she wanted to watch television.

1 'A policeman saw the accident.' (George/say)
2 'The shop sells newspapers, June.' (Harry/tell)
3 'I don't usually go to the cinema in the week.' (Mick/say)
4 'John painted the picture you like, Fred.' (Sally/tell)
5 'I can't find my tennis shoes, George.' (Don/tell)
6 'I'm going to plant a lot of flowers in this garden.' (Alice/say)
7 'John will want to see you, Peter.' (Tony/tell)
8 'I'm having dinner with Mary tonight.' (Alan/say)
9 'I'll take a taxi to the station.' (Anne/say)
10 'The film isn't very good, Kate.' (Maisie/tell)

5 Write the original statements

Write the original statements for these reported orders.

Example:

They told Tom to cook the dinner.

'Cook the dinner, Tom!'

1 He told Rosie to come home by ten o'clock.
2 She told Peter to buy the train tickets.
3 I told Victor to get some film for the camera.
4 He told her not to stop working.
5 She told him to walk faster.
6 They told Charlie not to go home early.
7 She told Fred not to drive too fast.
8 He told her to go to the doctor.
9 She told him to switch the light out.
10 He told her to get to work earlier.

6 Write reported statements or commands

Jim has felt ill and been to the doctor. Here he is reporting what the doctor said.

Example:

go home to bed! (command)

He told me to go home to bed.

must stay home for a week. (statement)

He said I had to stay home for a week.

1 am very ill (statement)
2 have the 'flu (statement)
3 stay in bed! (command)
4 drink some hot drinks! (command)
5 can read books (statement)
6 will feel very tired and cold (statement)
7 must keep my friends away (statement)
8 stop worrying about work! (command)
9 come back next week! (command)
10 take the medicine three times a day! (command)

Reported Speech 2: Questions (When People Ask Questions)
He asked Jane if she could help him

FORM

REPORTED QUESTIONS

1 When we report questions we use *ask* as the introductory (reporting) verb
She **asked** him if he was going to the cinema.
2 You always ask a person.
'Can you help me?'
When we report this question, we must know the name of the person the questioner was speaking to.
He asked **Jane** if she could help him.
3 The original question in 1 is *'Are you going to the cinema?'*.
When we report the question, we change the question into a statement.
'Do you play tennis in the summer?'
He asked her if **she played tennis in the summer**.
4 When the question needs a *yes* or *no* answer, we introduce the reported question with *if*.
She asked him **if** he was going to the cinema.
He asked Jane **if** she could help him.
He asked her **if** she played tennis in the summer.
5 When the question begins with a question word – *who, what, where, when, how,* etc.
we introduce the reported question with the original question word.

What are you doing tonight?
He asked her **what** she was doing tonight.
Where do you spend your holidays?
She asked him **where** he spent his holidays.
6 We make the following tense changes:
Present simple to past simple
'Do you come here often?' → He asked her if she came there often.
Present continuous to past continuous
'What are you doing?' → She asked him what he was doing.
Past simple or present perfect to past perfect.
'Where did you buy that dress?' → She asked her where she had bought that dress.
'Have you been to Italy?' → They asked him if he had been to Italy.
will becomes *would*
'Where will you be on 4th June?' → She asked him where he would be on 4th June.
can becomes *could*
'When can you help me with this exercise? → He asked her when she could help him with the exercise.

---

1 Match the questions

Match the reported questions to the original questions. The first one has been done for you.

1 He asked Bob if he was taking the exam in June.
2 He asked Jean where she was going.
3 He asked Sam if he would see him at the game.
4 He asked Myra if she could meet him in Paris.
5 He asked Mary if the football match had finished.
6 He asked Tom when he would get there.
7 He asked Pete how he cooked spaghetti.
8 He asked Jill if she liked fish.
9 He asked Joe what the name of the teacher was.
10 He asked Fred what he had done.
11 He asked Sally why she was working late.

a) 'Where are you going, Jean?'
b) 'When will you get there, Tom?'
c) 'How do you cook spaghetti, Pete?'
d) 'Are you taking the exam in June, Bob?'
e) 'Can you meet me in Paris, Myra?'
f) 'Why are you working late, Sally?'
g) 'What is the name of the teacher, Joe?'
h) 'What have you done, Fred?'
i) 'Will I see you at the game, Sam?'
j) 'Has the football match finished, Mary?'
k) 'Do you like fish, Jill?'

---

2 Write the question

Write the question that is being reported.
Example:
She asked Tom if he liked the painting.
Do you like the painting, Tom?

1 She asked Alan why he was going to Japan.
2 She asked Jill when she would arrive home.
3 She asked Emma what the film was like.
4 She asked Dave if he wanted to buy a new camera.
5 She asked Tony if he was tired.
6 She asked Anne why she wasn't at work.
7 She asked Jane where Terry lived.
8 She asked Fred if he had passed the exam.
9 She asked Mavis how she had gone to Moscow.

10 She asked Philip if he enjoyed sailing.

11 She asked Richard where he spent his holidays.

12 She asked Tom why he always went away at the weekend.

13 She asked Joan if she had already sold the house.

14 She asked Romy when she would finish the book.

15 She asked Paul if he was going to the party.

3 Write the reported questions

Write reported questions for the followings questions. Begin each sentence with He.

Example:
What's the woman at the bus stop doing, Sally?
He asked Sally what the woman at the bus stop was doing.

1 'How many cars are there in the car park, John?'
2 'Do you like ice-cream, Emma?'
3 'Is Egypt a big country, Roz?'
4 Where's the river Euphrates, Harry?
5 'How long will it take to get to London, Jack?'
6 'Is the meat fresh, Anne?'
7 'Will the train arrive on time, Kate?'
8 'Where's the nearest post office, Mavis?'
9 'Are there a lot of people at the meeting, Joe?'
10 'Why didn't you meet me at the station, Sam?'
11 'Are they showing a new film next week, Pete?'
12 'When are you coming to see me, Romy?'
13 'When do children go to school in your country, Ahmed?'
14 'Did the house burn down, Leslie?'
15 'Who stole your car, Mary?'

4 Write the original questions

Below are the answers to some of Bob's questions. Write the original questions as reported questions. The person named is the person Bob asked.

Example:
Alan: That book costs £25.
He asked Alan how much the book cost.

1 David: The best hotel is in King's Street.
2 Emma: I'll arrive at five o'clock.
3 Sally: No, I haven't seen Mary.
4 Harry: I took a taxi because I was late.
5 Pete: Yes, that's the cheapest shop here.
6 Anne: No, I didn't like the film.
7 Larry: Mars is the planet next to Earth.
8 Jane: These shoes cost £60.
9 John: I left school in 1994.

10 Lee: Tennis is my favourite game.

5 Write the reported questions

Last night there was a fight in the town. Frank Roberts saw the fight and had to go to the police station. When he got home, his family asked him what the police wanted to know. Below are the questions the police asked. Frank reported these questions to his family. Write down what Frank said.

Example:
What were you doing at eight o'clock?
They asked me what I was doing at eight o'clock.

1 When did you go to the bar?
2 Who did you meet in the bar?
3 How many people were in the bar?
4 Did you meet David Shaw there?
5 Do you like David Shaw?
6 How long have you known David Shaw?
7 Will you visit David Shaw in hospital?
8 What is your job?
9 What do you usually do in your free time?
10 Do you often go to that bar?
11 How much money do you owe David Shaw?
12 How much money do you earn each month?
13 Have you ever been to clubs with David Shaw?
14 Why did you borrow money from David Shaw?
15 Can you give David Shaw back his money?

6 Form reported questions

Tim has been to the police station. He is telling his friend what the police asked him.

Example:
what/my name/be
They asked me what my name was.
where/go/Friday night
They asked me where I went on Friday night.

1 what/my address/be
2 what time/leave/friend's house
3 when/arrive home
4 anyone/see me
5 who/see me
6 what/say
7 how many people/meet at my friends
8 why/leave early
9 always go to my friend's house on Fridays
10 How long/know this friend.

Question Tags
am I? can you? have they?

FORM

1 Look at these questions.
1 *You are going to Spain, **aren't you**?*
2 *David can't go out tonight, **can he**?*
3 *Jane's finished her homework, **hasn't she**?*
4 *Bill and Tom don't work very hard, **do they**?*

The part of the question in **bold** is called a 'question tag'. We make it by using the auxiliary or modal from the main sentence, followed by the pronoun for the subject of the main sentence. When there is no auxiliary in the main sentence, we use the verb *do*.

In 1 *You are* becomes *aren't you*
In 2 *David can't* becomes *can he*
In 3 *Jane's* becomes *hasn't she*
in 4 *Bill and Tom don't* becomes *do they*

Note:
We don't repeat the name of the person, but use the pronoun.

We make the question tag in the same way that we make the ordinary question.
But when the main sentence is positive, the question tag is usually negative.
*You **like** chocolate **don't** you?*
When the main sentence is negative, the question tag is usually positive.
*She **can't** spell well, **can** she?*
Note:
When the subject is **I** with the verb *to be* – *I'm seeing you tomorrow* – we usually use the plural form of the verb – *I'm seeing you tomorrow, **aren't I?***

USE

We use question tags when we want to check what we have said in the main sentence.
I'm seeing you tomorrow.
is a statement, but the speaker isn't sure, so checks:
I'm seeing you tomorrow, aren't I?

---

1 Complete the sentences

Complete the sentences by adding a question tag.
Example:
They aren't staying all the week, are they?

1 Mary works in Paris, ...?
2 You couldn't help me, ...?
3 We mustn't be late, ...?
4 I've met you before, ...?
5 The car doesn't go very fast, ...?
6 You've posted my letters, ...?
7 That shop stays open late on Thursdays, ...?
8 I'm catching the 10.15 train, ...?
9 The journey isn't very long, ...?
10 They went to Peru for their holiday, ...?
11 Jane didn't go out in the rain, ...?
12 That cat's very lively, ...?
13 He's leaving next month, ...?
14 She's going to work in Oman, ...?
15 Your daughter wants to be a nurse, ...?

2 Fill in the gaps

Fill in the gaps with a question tag. The first one has been done for you.

Paul: You went to Peru for your holiday, *didn't you*?
Mary: Yes, that's right.

Paul: They speak Spanish there, **(1)** ....?
Mary: Yes; but there are also some local languages.
Paul: Oh! You speak Spanish, **(2)** ....?
Mary: No, I don't.
Paul: That made it difficult for you, **(3)** ....?
Mary: No. It was all right. I was able to use English.
Paul: A lot of the people speak English, **(4)** ....?
Mary: A few.
Paul: It's a beautiful country, **(5)** ....?
Mary: I love it.
Paul: You worked there once, **(6)** ....?
Mary: Yes. Five years ago. You've been to South America, **(7)** ....?
Paul: No, never. But you've travelled a lot, **(8)** ....?
Mary: It was part of my job.
Paul: The Incas were in Peru, **(9)** ....?
Mary: A long time ago.
Paul: I know very little about the country. Bogota is the capital, **(10)** ....?
Mary: No that's in Colombia. Lima is the capital of Peru.
Paul: I should go there, **(11)** ....?
Mary: Yes. You'd love it.

Unit Revision Test 1

UNITS 1–11

Write the verb in the correct tense.

1 John always (go) swimming on Monday afternoons.
2 Mary never (work) after six o'clock.
3 John (watch) television at the moment.
4 He (telephone) you when the programme (finish).
5 I (play) football every Saturday but I don't now.
6 I (meet) him in the park yesterday afternoon.
7 He (look) very sad.
8 He (sit) on a bench by himself when I saw him.
9 I (visit) him tomorrow.
10 His parents (not give) him any money next month.
11 So he (work) in a shop next week.
12 The bus (arrive) at four o'clock.
13 I (take) my final exams next week.
14 (Visit) you your brother when you (be) in Australia next March?
15 They (sell) their house because they (live) in Italy.

UNITS 12–17

A *Complete the text with the correct modal verb.*

You (**16** necessity) to spend some time in Britain to improve your English. You (**17** advice) write to a company for a job. You will (**18** obligation) pay your fare to England, but you (**19** possibility) take your car, if you like. You (**20** not necessary) to have a job to go to Britain. You (**21** possibility) find one when you're there. But you (**22** prohibition) say that you are going for a holiday, if you are going to look for a job. When you get a job, you will (**23** obligation) pay tax. But you won't (**24** not obligatory) pay too much.

B *Write the correct verb to show a request or permission.*

John: (**25**) .... I borrow your book? (more polite)
Jane: Yes, of course, you (**26**) ....

Alan: (**27**) .... I have the car tonight? (most polite)
Sally: No, you (**28**) .... not.

Mary: (**29**) .... I call tomorrow night? (most used)
Richard: No, you .... (**30**).

UNITS 18–24

A *Replace the second sentence with a short sentence beginning with* so *or* nor.

31 John doesn't like fish. Mary doesn't like fish.
32 Mary worked in London. Peter worked in London.
33 Jane is very clever. David is very clever.

B *Write the verbs in the correct tense.*

34 If you (see) John in London, he (give) you some money for me.
35 If I (be) in Rome, I always (visit) the opera.
36 I (meet) you if I (be) at home. But I'm at work until eight o'clock.
37 These houses (build) by Adams in the eighteenth century.
38 The new road (open) by the President tomorrow.

C *Write the following as reported statements and questions.*

39 'Take that book home with you,' John told Keith.
40 'When are we going to buy a new television?' Mary asked David.
41 'That restaurant is very good,' said Peter.
42 'Don't do that!' Richard's mother told him.
43 'What are you doing on Friday?' Jane asked Tony.
44 'Did you like the film?' Alan asked Sally.
45 'I can't do this exercise,' Joan said.

D *Add question tags.*

46 It's a long journey, ...?
47 It gets very cold in winter, ...?
48 You can't swim that far, ...?
49 You didn't go to university in Italy, ...?
50 You must finish that work, ...?

UNIT 25 Articles: *the*, *a* / *an*, no article (ø)

USE

THE
1   when you know the person or thing you mean
the man next door
2   when you have talked about the person or thing before
I saw a man with a dog. The man was smiling.
3   when the thing or person is unique
the President, the sun
4   for countries that are a lot of states
the United States of America
5   for names of rivers, ranges of mountains
the Danube, the Urals

A/AN
1   when you are talking about a person or thing (singular) for the first time
I saw a man with a dog.
2   when it is something (singular) you can count
a pen, a book

NO ARTICLE (Ø)
1   when you are talking about people or things (plural) for the first time
I bought cakes and biscuits.
2   when it is something you can't count (singular or plural)
water, bread
3   for most countries
England, Spain, Turkey, America
4   for mountains
Mount Everest
Remember:
A before a consonant
a man, a girl
An before a vowel
an apple, an orange
Note:
You can use *what* + *a/an* or *no article* when you are happy and surprised:
What a lovely dress!
What lovely pictures!

1   Find the names

Find the names of six fruit and six things we wear or carry in the word-square below. Then write a *or* an *before them. Two have been done for you.*

G	S	I	L	M	T	X	J	U	O
R	P	Y	S	R	I	H	B	M	K
A	N	S	H	O	E	F	C	B	Z
P	I	K	D	R	E	S	S	R	O
E	L	I	I	A	P	P	L	E	N
W	H	R	T	N	D	U	E	L	E
V	B	T	C	G	I	U	M	L	P
O	G	I	P	E	A	R	O	A	Q
X	J	A	C	K	E	T	N	V	Q
P	S	B	A	V	O	C	A	D	O

Fruit   wear/carry
An avocado   *A tie*

. . . .

. . . .

. . . .

. . . .

. . . .

2   Write a, an or Ø (no article)

Examples:
The body of *a* whale lay on the beach.
In the fruit dish, there were *Ø* oranges, *Ø* pears, *a* banana and *an* apple.

1   John gave his girl-friend .... flowers for her birthday.
2   They met in ...... café near his college.
3   She ordered .... tea and .... sandwiches.
4   Afterwards he took her to see ..... action film.
5   ...... little girl fell down ..... well near the park gates.
6   She was lucky because ...... man heard her shouting.
7   He ran for .... policeman.
8   The policeman brought ..... rope with him.
9   He tied the rope to .... tree near the well.
10 .... woman came and saw the policeman rescue the little girl.
11 They had ..... fish for lunch.
12 He found ..... fifty pound note in the street.

Answers

UNIT 1
Exercise 1
1 Do lions run very fast?
2 Camels often go for days without water.
3 In some countries, people don't eat pork.
4 How much does a Rolls-Royce cost?
5 Fred always buys Japanese cars.
6 What films do you like?
7 Alice doesn't live here any more.
8 Do you love me?
9 He's very rich. He doesn't need any money.
10 The sun rises in the east.
11 We sometimes have parties.
12 Does he have a television?
13 Who lives in this house?
14 Does she like playing sport?
15 They usually go home at Christmas.
Exercise 3
1 Where do you live? 2 live 3 Do you like...? 4 What do you do? 5 teach 6 sell 7 don't like 8 want 9 Do you prefer ...? 10 What do you teach?

UNIT 2
Exercise 1
1 are flying 2 is looking 3 is writing 4 is painting 5 is travelling 6 is walking 7 are wearing 8 is ringing 9 are playing 10 is raining, I'm getting 11 is reading 12 is running
Exercise 2
1 aren't fighting 2 isn't writing 3 isn't playing 4 isn't printing 5 aren't flying 6 I'm not getting 7 isn't taking 8 aren't making 9 isn't sailing 10 aren't living 11 isn't working 12 isn't raining
Exercise 3
1 What's Charlie studying at university?
2 What's Jane learning?
3 Is Paul playing tennis?
4 Are Sally and Rosie still singing with a rock group?
5 Where's David meeting his girl-friend?
6 What's Tony teaching at university?
7 How fast are we now travelling?
8 What are Maria and Tim doing this week?
9 Where are they building new houses?
10 What are they showing at that cinema?
11 Where is Jane working this year?
12 Is Alan visiting one of his patients?
13 What's John buying?
14 When are Tom and Anne taking their holiday?
15 Are they leaving at 6 o'clock?

UNIT 3
Exercise 1
1 is playing, plays 2 nest, eat 3 is coming 4 comes 5 Is Peter eating, doesn't usually eat 6 is snowing, snows 7 am celebrating, celebrate 8 is showing, show 9 is going, am getting up, live, does she live 10 carry, fly, does it take
Exercise 2
1 John usually goes to the office, but today he's working at home.
2 You usually work late, but today you're leaving early.
3 Alan usually meets his friend Betty, but today he's meeting Sally.
4 Sarah usually has lunch at 12 o'clock, but today she's having lunch at 2 o'clock
5 I usually drive my car to work, but today I'm going by train.
6 Lucy usually wears a dress, but today she's wearing trousers.
7 Keith usually catches a bus to work, but today he's catching a train.
8 Kate and Dick usually swim before breakfast, but today they're doing their homework.
9 Tony usually spends the evening at home, but today he's going to a party.
10 We usually watch the late news on TV, but today we're listening to a radio play.
11 Phillip usually eats meat, but today he's eating fish.
12 They usually play football, but today they're watching it on TV.
13 She usually reads a book at lunch-time, but today she's reading a magazine.
14 Anne usually phones her customers, but today she's visiting them.
15 I usually walk home but today I'm taking a taxi.
Exercise 3:
1 live 2 are building 3 are buying 4 fly 5 drive 6 are staying 7 live 8 like, don't go 9 are coming 10 are going
Exercise 4
1 goes 2 is she going 3 She's carrying 4 carries 5 She's going 6 What does she do? 7 Why are we following 8 lives 9 does she find 10 Does she rob 11 is robbing 12 she's running 13 are coming 14 They're shouting
Exercise 5
1 stand 2 have 3 look 4 is putting 5 are sitting 6 are waiting 7 a table 8 have 9 fly 10 make 11 hurt 12 live 13 kills 14 am playing 15 am trying 16 is attacking 17 a bee 18 am running 19 am looking 20 run 21 am making 22 do not like/don't like 23 have 24 see 25 jump 26 a dog.

UNIT 4
Exercise 1
1 discovered 2 went 3 found 4 brought 5 didn't look 6 didn't talk 7 tried 8 didn't win, won 9 bought 10 made.
Exercise 2
1 was, didn't know, lay was 2 were, climbed, started, gave.
Exercise 3
1 Who did she meet?
2 What was his job?
3 What did they do?
4 What did he promise?
5 What did she do when she got home?
6 Who wrote the first letter?
7 What happened after two weeks?
8 Who wrote that letter?

UNIT 5
Exercise 1
1 was watching 2 was studying 3 was playing 4 Were you staying 5 weren't waiting 6 were looking 7 Were you speaking 8 was talking 9 was cleaning 10 was checking
Exercise 2
1 was crossing 2 were crossing 3 were coming 4 was racing 5 was coming 6 was going 7 were looking 8 were having 9 Was riding 10 was going 11 was running 12 was shouting 13 What was the owner shouting? 14 was telling 15 Were the car drivers going 16 was selling 17 was buying 18 was talking 19 why were you crossing 20 were coming

UNIT 6
Exercise 1
1 was building 2 stayed 3 heard 4 lived 5 came 6 was playing 7 came 8 were putting 9 shot 10 were driving.
Exercise 2
1 was doing, came 2 saw, wasn't working, was sleeping 3 came, were playing 4 didn't hear, were playing 5 was barking, came 6 was watching, arrived 7 was studying, began 8 wasn't hunting, shot 9 were playing, started 10 was giving, left
Exercise 3
1 What were they doing when they saw the monkeys?
   What did they see when they were visiting the zoo?
2 What was Joan doing when she hurt her leg?
   What did Joan do when she was climbing in the mountains?
3 What were you doing when you bought this perfume? Where were you staying when you bought this perfume?
   What did you buy while you were staying in Paris?
4 What was Charlie doing when he met some old friends?
   Who did Charlie meet while he was working in Spain?
5 What was Richard doing when the burglars came in?
   What happened while Richard was sleeping?
6 What were they doing when the swan attacked them?
   What did the swan do while they were fishing in the canal?
7 What were they doing when the manager sold the club?
   What did the manager do while they were playing an important football match?
8 What was Simon doing when his friend George took his clothes away?
   What did George do while Simon was swimming in the river?
9 What were Anne and Carl doing when they got married? Where were Anne and Carl living when they got married?
   What did Anne and Carl do while they were living in Mexico?
10 What was he doing when lots of people came to see him?
   What did lots of people do while he was painting the picture?
Exercise 4
1 was going to school/learned to drive 2 was living in London 3 was working in a shop in Berlin 4 bought a house in Oxford 5 married Frances 6 was studying history 7 was teaching English in Oxford 8 met Andrew 9 was travelling round the world with Andrew 10 became a father
Exercise 5
1 were laughing 2 ringing 3 came 4 phoned 5 heard 6 saw 7 was going 8 was following 9 stopped 10 got out 11 jumped 12 took
Exercise 6
1 left, finished, closed 2 was walking, met 3 bought, were waiting, saw 4 met, arrived 5 told 6 felt/was, feeling, were eating 7 went, saw 8 were shouting 9 hit 10 was crying, took

UNIT 7
Exercise 1
1 used to 2 used to 3 used to 4 used to 5 didn't use to 6 Did you use to 7 used to 8 used to 9 didn't use to 10 used to 11 used to 12 didn't use to 13 used to 14 Did you use to 15 didn't use to.
Exercise 2
1 used to be 2 used to be 3 used to go 4 used to walk 5 used to enjoy 6 saw 7 were 8 wanted 9 met 10 got 11 used to go 12 left

UNIT 8
Exercise 1
2 has returned 3 (has) stayed 4 has made 5 have bought 6 have always welcomed 7 have travelled 8 has climbed 9 (has) seen
Exercise 2
1 Have you finished painting the house yet?
   No, I haven't done it yet. But I've painted all the inside walls.
2 I haven't seen Geoffrey today.
   He's gone to London.
   Has he been there before?
3 Mary has broken those beautiful glasses.
   Has she told her mother? Her mother hasn't got any more.
4 Has John brought the food?
   No, he hasn't been to the shop yet. He's lost his money.
5 Has Daisy passed her exam?
   Yes, she's won a scholarship but she hasn't decided what to do.
Exercise 3
2 Jane's married 3 they've never talked 4 they've both travelled 5 they've been 6 Has she known?

UNIT 9
Exercise 1
VERB	PAST SIMPLE	PAST PARTICIPLE
become	became	become
build	built	built
buy	bought	bought
come	came	come
fall	fell	fallen
go	went	gone
hang	hung	hung
have	had	had
hear	heard	heard
know	knew	known
let	let	let
read	read	read
run	ran	run
see	saw	seen
sell	sold	sold
sing	sang	sung
take	took	taken
understand	understood	understood
win	won	won
write	wrote	written

Exercise 2
1 took 2 taught 3 passed 4 have just seen 5 have had 6 bought 7 has been 8 has read 9 lived, went 10 painted 11 bought, has lived 12 passed 13 met 14 have visited 15 went
Exercise 3
1 Yes, I have. I went there in 1994.
2 Yes, I have. I saw her last May.
3 No, I haven't. But my father built this one in 1952.
4 Yes, she has. She finished it ten minutes ago.
5 Yes, he has. He invited them last week.
6 Yes, they have. They were there in 1995.
7 No, he hasn't. But his wife flew in one two years ago.
8 No, I haven't. But my neighbour won £3 million last September.
9 Yes, it has. It started ten minutes ago.
10 Yes, I have. I finished it yesterday.
11 Yes, she has. She arrived two hours ago.

A

12 Yes, they have. They had one for ten years.

13 Yes, I have. I found it in my suit-case.

14 No, she hasn't. But her brother visited them last month.

15 No, I haven't. But my boyfriend saw it last night and really liked it.

Exercise 4

1 Did you see John when you were in Berlin?

2 How did you go to Cambridge?

3 When did Dolly last sing a popular song?

4 Have Pete and Dave climbed all the hills in England?

5 How many crime books has Fred written?

6 Did you drive too fast?

7 How many of his 1960s records has John sold?

8 How many times has the telephone rung for me?

9 How long have you waited here?

10 Did she win the swimming race?

11 Has Anne phoned yet?

12 When did you read his books?

13 How long have they been in the restaurant?

14 Where does your father live?

15 Have they found a new house yet?

Exercise 5

1 was 2 made 3 took 4 became 5 wasn't 6 closed 7 came 8 fought 9 has changed 10 have had 11 has attacked 12 have had 13 has been 14 has built 15 has fallen 16 has connected 17 didn't allow 18 was

UNIT 10

Exercise 1

Mattie: Now, Tom. *You're going to finish* at university in June. What are you going to do?

Tom: I'm going to travel round the world.

Mattie: Are you going to have enough money?

Tom: I think so. I'm going to get a job in the summer and I'm going to save some money. I'm not going to need a lot of money.

Mattie: When are you going to start travelling?

Tom: In October. I'm going to sail across the Atlantic to Brazil.

Mattie: Are you going to buy a boat?

Tom: No. I'm going to work on a ship.

Mattie: You're going to have an exciting time.

Exercise 2

1 Next year I'll be twenty four.

2 We'll have a new President in May.

3 I won't be able to come next week.

4 It'll be very cold next winter.

5 It's very early. There won't be anyone at home yet.

6 I'll learn to swim next year.

7 It's a horror film. He won't like it.

8 She's very clever. She'll pass the exams easily.

9 He'll be head of the department soon.

10 They drive very fast. They'll have an accident.

Exercise 3

2 f 3 b 4 c 5 a 6 e

2 intention 3 prediction with evidence 4 intention 5 prediction with evidence 6 intention

Exercise 4

2 e 3 f 4 a 5 b 6 d

2 prediction with evidence 3 prediction with evidence 4 intention 5 offer 6 intention

Exercise 5:

1 F 2 B 3 C 4 A 5C 6 A 7 C 8 C 9 C 10 G

Exercise 6

1 You'll enjoy that film.

2 The sky's clear tonight it's going to be cold.

3 She's going to visit Greece in the autumn.

4 She has promised that she'll see you next week.

5 I'll talk to her in the morning.

6 They're going to get married in May.

7 He's going to be an engineer.

8 They'll be here at nine.

9 I like hot countries, so I'm going to like Tunisia.

10 She's going to borrow the book from the library. She always does.

UNIT 11

Exercise 1

1 A 2 C 3 B 4 A 5 B 6 A 7 C 8 C 9 C 10 A

Exercise 2

1 On Sunday 17th June at 12.30 p.m., he's having lunch with Andrew.

2 On Monday 18th June at 11 a.m., David's meeting John Roberts.

3 At 12.30 p.m., he's having lunch with Andrew.

4 At 6 p.m., he's playing tennis.

5 On Thursday 21st June, he's going to the theatre in the evening.

6 On Saturday 23rd June, he's doing the garden in the morning.

7 In the evening, he's going to Alice's party.

8 On Tuesday 26th June, he's driving to London.

9 On Wednesday 27th June, he's attending a business meeting at 8.00 a.m.

10 He's returning home at 6.00 p.m.

Exercise 3

1 leaves 2 opens 3 John's having 4 they're giving 5 I'm working 6 come 7 starts 8 I'm having 9 opens 10 She's leaving. 11 They're going 12 go 13 we're having 14 goes 15 eat 16 close 17 take 18 we're going 19 he's buying 20 Mary's leaving

Exercise 4

1 When I see Richard, I'll tell him about your new job.

2 If you arrive early, you'll be able to watch the parade.

3 The game will be over before you reach the stadium.

4 They'll sell their house if they find a good buyer.

5 As soon as David learns the results of the exam, he'll look for a job.

6 When he gets a job, he'll buy a house.

7 After he buys a house, he'll get a car.

8 If he gets a car, he'll learn to drive.

9 After he learns to drive, he'll visit his girl-friend in Greece.

10 If he goes to Greece, he'll get married.

11 If she passes her exams, she'll go to university.

12 When I get to work, I'll phone you.

13 After they return from India, they'll take a rest.

14 I'll stop work if I win the lottery.

15 Dinner will be ready when we get home

Exercise 5

Greg: What are you doing on Saturday?

Sally: I'm going to the theatre. Why?

Greg: I'm having a party. I'd like you to come.

Sally: That's difficult. John's buying the tickets this afternoon.

Greg: Come afterwards. What time does the play finish?

Sally: I'm not sure. It starts at 7.30. It's about 2 hours long.

Greg: Then you could come at ten. It's important because I'm leaving for China on Monday.

Sally: Why are you going there?

Greg: I'm working there for the next two years.

Sally: Two years. Then I'm coming for a holiday

UNIT 12

Exercise 1

1 You don't have to pay for them now.

2 Do they need to finish the painting today?/Need they finish the painting today?

3 Must you catch the late train?

4 He mustn't see you here.

5 Everyone has to eat.

6 Do we have to go there?

7 We must all leave the building immediately.

8 You don't need to book your seat for the theatre./ You needn't book your seat for the theatre.

9 They're very rich. They don't have to work.

10 You need to get a car. The public transport is bad.

11 It's raining. You need to take an umbrella with you.

12 She doesn't have to come in early every day.

13 You must find that money. It's mine!

14 I need at least eight hours sleep every night.

15 She doesn't need to work so hard.

Exercise 2

1 must 2 doesn't have (to) 3 Must 4 have (to) 5 don't have (to) 6 Do we have (to) 7 must 8 must(n't) 9 must 10 Do I have (to) 11 Does she have (to) 12 must 13 must 14 doesn't have to 15 Does Jenny have (to)

Exercise 3

1 needs 2 doesn't need 3 Need 4 need 5 don't need 6 Do we need 7 need to 8 need(n't) 9 need to 10 Do I need 11 Does she need 12 needs 13 needs 14 doesn't need to 15 Does Jenny need (to)

Exercise 4

1 must/have to 2 mustn't 3 must/have to 4 need to/have to 5 mustn't 6 mustn't 7 needn't/don't need to/don't have to 8 need to/have to 9 needn't/don't need to/don't have to 10 needn't/don't need to/don't have to 11 needs to/has to 12 must/have to 13 mustn't 14 must 15 need to/have to

Exercise 5

1 You must/have to arrive before eight o'clock.

2 You must/have to wear the correct clothes. ...

3 You needn't/don't need to/don't have to pay every time.

4 You mustn't bring your wife. ...

5 You need/have to buy a car. ...

6 You needn't/don't need to/don't have to have your own horse.

7 You mustn't go on the course before a big race.

8 You needn't/don't need to/don't have to live in the town.

9 You mustn't bring your own food into this restaurant.

10 You must/have to have lunch before half-past one.

11 You need/have to wear formal clothes to this party.

12 You mustn't smoke in many restaurants now.

13 You needn't/don't need to/don't have to ...

14 You mustn't take photographs here.

15 You must/have to pay before you go in.

UNIT 13

Exercise 1

1 can 2 couldn't 3 are able 4 wasn't able 5 can 6 couldn't 7 will be able 8 can 9 couldn't 10 can

Exercise 2

Were you able ... 2 Can/could Penny ... 3 How can a man ... 4 Were they really able to ... 5 Can you ... 6 Could people ... 7 Where can you ... 8 How long is a man able to ... 9 When will we be able to see ... 10 What could you see ...

Exercise 3

1 can't 2 can 3 can 4 can't 5 could 6 can/could 7 Can/Could 8 can't/couldn't 9 are able 10 can

Exercise 4

1 D 2 B 3 E 4 F 5 E 6 A 7 A 8 G 9 A 10 C

Exercise 5

1 You can't park between ...

2 Non-residents can use the hotel restaurant.

3 Children under 12 can't come in.

4 You can't smoke in the air terminal.

5 You can use foreign currency here.

6 They can't refund your money for unused tickets./ If you don't use your tickets, you can't get your money back.

7 Women only can come into this room.

8 You can choose your own fish ...

9 You can't have a meal after 10 o'clock.

10 You can use your membership card for the swimming in the gym.

UNIT 14

Exercise 1

1 may 2 might 3 May 4 may 5 may have 6 might have 7 might 8 May 9 might 10 may

Exercise 2

1 May I use the 'phone?

2 May I borrow your bicycle?

3 May I go home early?

4 May I watch television?

5 May I listen to the radio?

6 May I have dinner early?

7 May I borrow your course book?

8 May I open the window?

9 May I buy a new pair of shoes?

10 May I drive the car?

Exercise 3

1 A 2 D 3 E 4 C 5 B 6 A 7 C 8 F 9 D 10 E

Exercise 4

1 may have 2 may 3 may have 4 may have 5 may 6 may have 7 may 8 may have 9 may have 10 may

Exercise 5
1 might 2 may 3 might 4 May 5 may
6 may 7 may 8 might 9 may 10 may
Exercise 6
1 might 2 might 3 may 4 may
5 may 6 may 7 may 8 may 9 might
10 may 11 may 12 might

UNIT 15
Exercise 1
1 Could 2 can't 3 might 4 may
5 could 6 might 7 may 8 Can 9 may
10 could
Exercise 2:
1 Can I go to the cinema?
2 May I use the computer?
3 May I go home early?
4 Could I see your birthday present?
5 May I have a party next week?
6 Can I go on a ski-trip to the mountains?
7 Could I go swimming?
8 May I close the door?
9 Can I have a day's holiday on Thursday?
10 May I drive the car?

UNIT 16
Exercise 1
1 can't/mustn't 2 can't/mustn't 3 can't/mustn't
4 can't 5 mustn't 6 can't 7 mustn't
8 mustn't 9 can't 10 can't
Exercise 2
1 refusing permission ( ) 2 a rule (X)
3 a rule (X) 4 refusing permission ( )
5 a rule (X) 6 a rule (X) 7 refusing permission ( ) 8 a rule (X) 9 refusing permission ( ) 10 a rule (X)
Exercise 3
1 You can't/mustn't smoke in this restaurant.
2 You can't/mustn't drink in here after 11 p.m.
3 Children under fourteen can't come in.
4 You can't/mustn't bring guns in.
5 You can't come in after 5.45.
6 You mustn't drink and drive.
7 You mustn't get on the train without a ticket.
8 You mustn't stand too close to the paintings.

UNIT 17
Exercise 1
1 should 2 ought 3 Should 4 shouldn't
5 Ought 6 ought not 7 should 8 should
9 should 10 ought 11 should
12 shouldn't:
Exercise 2
1 Should they clean their car more often?
2 When should they be here?
3 Ought he to telephone her?
4 How often should the students do their homework?
5 When should students hand in their work?
6 Ought he to work so hard?
7 Ought they to spend so much money on their child?
8 When should they finish the work?
9 Should he have spoken to her like that?
10 Ought they to have finished by now?
11 How often should she go to the hospital?
12 Ought he to go out every lunch-time?
Exercise 3:
1 B 2 B 3 D 4 D 5 C 6 B
7 C 8 A 9 C 10 C 11 E 12 D
Exercise 4
1 should 2 should 3 should 4 ought
5 should 6 ought 7 should 8 should
9 should 10 should 11 shouldn't
12 should

Exercise 5
1 should I tell
2 should not/shouldn't have lied
3 should be
4 should always tell
5 should not/shouldn't have taken
6 should have asked
7 should not/shouldn't be
8 should not/shouldn't want
9 should buy
10 should always look

UNIT 18
Exercise 1
2 f 3 e 4 a 5 b 6 j 7 k 8 c 9 g 10 i 11 d.
Exercise 2
1 Neither will we. 2 Nor do I. 3 So are those in Mary's garden. 4 So does Iran. 5 So is Tokyo. 6 So can Kate. 7 Nor would I. 8 So did I. 9 Nor did we. 10 So have I. 11 So have they. 12 Nor have we. 13 So do I. 14 So does she. 15 Neither can we. 16 So is Anne. 17 So can I. 18 Nor has he. 19 Neither did we. 20 So do I.
Exercise 3
1 Neither 2 So 3 So 4 Neither 5 So 6 Neither 7 So 8 Neither 9 Neither 10 So, 11 Neither/nor 12 Niether/nor 13 So 14 Neither 15 Neither
Exercise 4
1 So is Sri Lanka. 2 Nor is Brazil. 3 So does Sri lanka. 4 Nor is Sri lanka. 5 So does Brazil. 6 So is Britain. 7 Nor is Brazil. 8 So is Spain. 9 Nor is Britain. 10 So has Brazil.
Exercise 5
1 was I 2 did I 3 did I 4 did I 5 did I 6 have I 7 am I 8 have I 9 did mine 10 do I.

UNIT 19
Exercise 1
1 e 2 i 3 f 4 j 5 c 6 a 7 h 8 k 9 d 10 b 11 g
Exercise 2
1 Mary won't like it if you come late.
2 If they pass the exam, they'll have a big party.
3 They'll lose if they don't get better players.
4 I'll help her if she wants me to.
5 That hotel will be cheaper if you go in March.
6 If she gets the job, she'll earn a lot of money.
7 If you go to Sydney at Christmas, it'll be very hot.
8 They'll sell the business if they get more customers.
9 If you dress well, they'll give you the job.
10 You'll have an interview if you apply before next week.
Exercise 3:
1 B 2 A 3 A 4 B 5 A 6 A 7 B 8 A 9 B 10 A
Exercise 4
1 If I lend him the money, he'll be able to have a holiday.
2 If I watch television late at night, I fall asleep.
3 If they have a party, all the neighbours get angry.
4 The boss'll be angry if you leave early.
5 You'll arrive too early if you take the 9 o'clock train.
6 If you arrive early, you have to wait outside.
7 If you finish the work on time, I'll take you to a good restaurant.
8 If it's hot, they go to their house by the sea.
9 If it rains, I won't go to the tennis match today.
10 If it rains, they cancel the game.

Exercise 5
1 He sees the Queen 2 They'll be miserable 3 I'll go to the party alone 4 I'll buy a new car 5 She'll marry him 6 I take the bus 7 I'll stay at home 8 I'll swim in the lake 9 She'll have a holiday 10 I call the garage 11 She's angry 12 I'll go to the cinema 13 I go by train 14 He'll stay in Italy 15 I run down the fire-escape.

UNIT 20
Exercise 1
2 e 3 h 4 i 5 g 6 a 7 k 8 j 9 c 10 d 11 b.
Exercise 2
1 Jack wouldn't like it if you did better than him in the exam.
2 If you passed the exam, you'd be the youngest person in the top class.
3 If you failed the exam, you'd be able to take it again next year.
4 I'd buy a house by the sea if I lived in Greece.
5 If you bought a house by the sea, you'd have lots of problems.
6 The house would be in danger if there was a bad storm.
7 I wouldn't live by the sea if you paid me £2 million.
8 They'd be very happy if he played in the concert.
9 If they tell the people about him, many people will come to the concert.
10 If many people came to the concert, they'd get a lot of money.
Exercise 3
1 A 2 A 3 B 4 B 5 B 6 B 7 B 8 A 9 A 10 A
Exercise 4
1 went, gave 2 broke, wouldn't know 3 went, she'd have 4 ate, was 5 took, travelled 6 was/were, I'd play 7 rained, didn't go 8 was, played 9 went, you'd have to 10 bought, wouldn't have
Exercise 5
1 She'd marry a rich man 2 They were very miserable 3 She'd find a new boy-friend 4 I called the rescue service 5 He'd have to work 6 I walked to work 7 I'd learn the language 8 I'd have a big house in Hollywood 9 I'd go to Mars 10 I called the police

UNIT 21
Exercise 1
1 be left 2 are allowed 3 were done 4 are checked 5 are trained 6 be collected 7 be finished 8 be sent 9 are taught 10 are cleaned
Exercise 2
1 The dinner was cooked by Jane.
2 That book was written by Robin.
3 That table was made by me.
4 The marathon will be won by Alan.
5 The road was built in 1987.
6 Those trees were planted in 1915.
7 Mary was given that expensive diamond ring by John.
or
That expensive diamond ring was given to Mary by John.
8 The television and video were stolen last week.
9 Mt Everest was first climbed in 1953.
10 The last cake in the shop was bought by Peter.
Exercise 3
1 was seen, talked 2 have made, are sold 3 wasn't seen, took 4 was posted, wasn't delivered 5 contained, was lost 6 is owned, drives 7 was made, was written 8 travel, are given 9 were put, heard 10 was given, sold

Exercise 4
1 The photographs of the wedding were taken by Robin last week.
2 Daisy will paint her house next month.
3 That boy is allowed to stay up late by his parents.
4 You mustn't play games in this park.
5 That table was made by my father ten years ago.
6 The World Cup was won by Italy in 1982.
7 That building was destroyed by fire last month.
8 This work can be done by one man.
9 Richard caught the thief when he was shopping in the High Street.
10 The window was broken by a boy this morning.
Exercise 5
1 be given 2 was painted 3 was done 4 Was it shown 5 will be seen 6 be hung 7 will be lit 8 Has it been bought 9 be seen 10 is sold/has been sold

UNIT 22
Exercise 1
1 e 2 f 3 d 4 h 5 k 6 a 7 j 8 g 9 b 10 i 11 c
Exercise 2
1 David said his brother was living in Istanbul.
2 Mary said David couldn't get a ticket for the concert.
3 Sam said the bell didn't work.
4 He told Fred not to break that chair.
5 Rosie told Alan to bring her that book.
6 Daisy said she would be in London then.
7 Harry said the train was late.
8 Jill said she was going to visit her mother in August.
9 Alec and Dan said they wanted to see the play at the local theatre.
10 Ken said he was too old to play football in the park.
Exercise 3
1 'I don't like tomatoes.'
2 'We're buying the house at the corner of the street.'
3 'I won't be here during January.'
4 'The flowers are beautiful.'
5 'The football team plays badly.'
6 'I can't come.'
7 'I haven't been to Italy since 1995.'
8 'I don't watch television.'
9 'I've lost/I lost all my money on the train.'
10 We always listen to the news at eight o'clock.
Exercise 4
1 George said a policeman had seen the accident.
2 Harry told June (that) the shop sold newspapers.
3 Mick said he didn't usually go to the cinema in the week.
4 Sally told Fred (that) John had painted the picture he liked.
5 Don told George he couldn't find his tennis shoes.
6 Alice said she was going to plant a lot of flowers in that garden.
7 Tony told Peter (that) John would want to see him.
8 Alan said that he was having dinner with Mary that night.
9 Anne said she would take a taxi to the station.
10 Maisie told Kate the film wasn't very good.

Exercise 5
1 'Come home by ten o'clock, Rosie!'
2 'Buy the train tickets, Peter!'
3 'Get some film for the camera, Victor!'
4 'Don't stop working!'
5 'Walk faster!'
6 'Don't go home early, Charlie!'
7 'Don't drive too fast, Fred!'
8 'Go to the doctor!'
9 'Switch the light out!'
10 'Get to work earlier!'

Exercise 6
1 He said I was very ill.
2 He said I had the 'flu.
3 He told me to stay in bed.
4 He told me to drink some hot drinks.
5 He said I could read books.
6 He said I would feel very tired and cold.
7 He said I had to keep my friends away.
8 He told me to stop worrying about work.
9 He told me to come back next week.
10 He told me to take the medicine three times a day.

UNIT 23
Exercise 1
1 d 2 a 3 i 4 e 5 j 6 b 7 c 8 k 9 g 10 h 11 f.

Exercise 2
1 Why are you going to Japan, Alan?
2 When will you arrive home, Jill?
3 What was the film like, Emma?
4 Do you want to buy a new camera, Dave?
5 Are you tired, Tony?
6 Why aren't you at work, Anne?
7 Where does Terry live, Jane?
8 Did you pass the exam, Fred?
9 How did you go to Moscow, Mavis?
10 Do you enjoy sailing, Philip?
11 Where do you spend your holidays, Richard?
12 Why do you always go away at the weekend, Tom?
13 Have you already sold the house, Joan?
14 When will you finish the book, Romy?
15 Are you going to the party, Paul?

Exercise 3
1 He asked John how many cars there were in the car park.
2 He asked Emma, if she liked ice-cream.
3 He asked Roz if Egypt was a big country.
4 He asked Harry where the River Euphrates was.
5 He asked Jack how long it would take to get to London.
6 He asked Anne if the meat was fresh.
7 He asked Kate if the train would arrive on time.
8 He asked Mavis where the nearest post office was.
9 He asked Joe if there were a lot of people at the meeting.
10 He asked Sam why he hadn't met him at the station.
11 He asked Pete if they were showing a new film the next week.
12 He asked Romy when she was coming to see him.
13 He asked Ahmed when children went to school in his country.
14 He asked Leslie if the house had

burnt down.
15 He asked Mary who had stolen her car.

Exercise 4
1 He asked David where the best hotel was.
2 He asked Emma when she would arrive.
3 He asked Sally if she had seen Mary.
4 He asked Harry why he had taken a taxi.
5 He asked Pete if that was the cheapest shop there.
6 He asked Anne if she liked the film.
7 He asked Larry what the name of the planet next to Earth was.
8 He asked Jane how much the shoes had cost.
9 He asked John when he had left school.
10 He asked Lee what his favourite game was.

Exercise 5
1 They asked me when I had gone to the bar.
2 They asked me who I had met in the bar.
3 They asked me how many people had been in the bar.
4 They asked me if I had met David Shaw there.
5 They asked me if I liked David Shaw.
6 They asked me how long I had known David Shaw.
7 They asked me if I would visit David Shaw in hospital.
8 They asked me what my job was.
9 They asked me what I usually did in my free time.
10 They asked me if I often went to the bar.
11 They asked me how much money I owed David Shaw.
12 They asked me how much money I earned each month.
13 They asked me if I had ever been to clubs with David Shaw.
14 They asked me why I had borrowed money from David Shaw.
15 They asked me if I could give David Shaw back his money.

Exercise 6
1 They asked me what my address was.
2 They asked me what time I left my friend's house.
3 They asked me when I arrived home.
4 They asked me if anyone saw me.
5 They asked me who saw me.
6 They asked me what I said.
7 They asked me how many people I met at my friend's house.
8 They asked me why I left early.
9 They asked me if I always went to my friend's on Fridays.
10 They asked me how long I had known this friend.

UNIT 24
Exercise 1
1 doesn't she 2 could you 3 must we 4 haven't I 5 does it 6 haven't you 7 doesn't it 8 aren't I 9 is it 10 didn't they 11 did she 12 isn't it 13 isn't he 14 isn't she 15 doesn't she.

Exercise 2
1 don't they 2 don't you 3 didn't it 4 don't they 5 isn't it 6 didn't you 7 haven't you 8 haven't you 9 weren't they 10 isn't it 11 shouldn't I

Units 1–11
1 goes 2 works 3 is watching 4 will telephone, has finished 5 used to play 6 met 7 looked/was looking 8 was sitting 9 I'll visit 10 won't give 11 is going 12 arrives 13 take 14 Will you visit, are 15 are selling, are going to live

Units 12–17
A
16 need/have to 17 should 18 have to 19 can 20 don't need 21 can 22 mustn't 23 have to 24 have to
B
25 Could 26 can 27 May 28 may 29 Can 30 can't

Units 18–24
A
31 Nor does Mary. 32 So does Peter. 33 So is David.
B
34 see, 'll give 35 am, visit. 36 'd meet, was/were 37 were built 38 will be opened
C
39 John told Keith to take that book home with him. 40 Mary asked David when they were going to buy a new television. 41 Peter said that restaurant was very good. 42 Richard's mother told him not to do that. 43 Jane asked Tony what he was doing on Friday. 44 Alan asked Sally if she liked the film. 45 Joan said she couldn't do this exercise.
D
46 isn't it 47 doesn't it 48 can you 49 did you 50 mustn't you.

UNIT 25
Exercise 1
an apple, a grape, a lemon, an orange, a pear
a dress, a jacket, a shoe, a skirt, an umbrella

Exercise 2
1 ø, 2 a, 3 ø, ø, 4 an, 5 A, a, 6 a, 7 a, 8 a, 9 a, 10 A, 11 ø, 12 a, 13 ø, 14 a, 15 a.

Exercise 3
1 an 2 the 3 the 4 a 5 a 6 the 7 the 8 a 9 The 10 the 11 a 12 the 13 The 14 a 15 a 16 the/ø 17 ø

Exercise 4
1 The 2 the 3a 4 ø 5 a 6 the 7 the 8 a 9 a 10 a

Exercise 5
1 A 2 A, A 3 C 4 B 5 C 6 E 7 C, B 8 C 9 A, C, E 10 A 11 B 12 B 13 B 14 C 15 A, A, A, A, A

UNIT 26
Exercise 1

PERSON	POSSESSIVE ADJECTIVE	POSSESSIVE PRONOUN
I	my	mine
You	your	yours
He	his	his
She	her	hers
It	its	—
We	our	ours
They	their	theirs

Exercise 2
1 his 2 my 3 their 4 his 5 their 6 her 7 her 8 his 9 my 10 your 11 our 12 his 13 our 14 her 15 their

Exercise 3
1 That car's his. 2 Those shoes are hers. 3 Those dirty clothes are yours. 4 The fields behind our house are his. 5 That house over there is his. 6 The boat over there is his. 7 This company is his. 8 That restaurant is theirs. 9 That furniture is theirs. 10 That football is his. 11 That boat is ours. 12 Those cars over there are theirs.

13 All the land round here is hers. 14 That book is ours. 15 Those shops in the High Street are his.

Exercise 4
1 Those are Mary's flowers./Those flowers are Mary's.
2 That's the college's television. /That television is the college's.
3 Those are the Institute's computers./Those computers are the Institute's.
4 It's the members' football club./The football club is the members'.
5 That's Alice's typewriter./That typewriter is Alice's.
6 That's my father's shop./That shop is my father's.
7 This is the President's land./This land is the President's.
8 That's Dracula's castle./That castle is Dracula's.
9 Those are the farmer's cows./Those cows are the farmer's.
10 That's Matthew's coat./That coat's Matthew's.

Exercise 5
1 yours 2 mine 3 hers/Daisy's 4 hers 5 Mary's 6 Her 7 his 8 his 9 his/her/their 10 his

UNIT 27
Exercise 1
1(a) these (b) those 2 this 3 that 4 this 5 That 6 That 7 those 8 that 9 (a) this (b) those 10 that

Exercise 2
1 This 2 that 3 this 4 that 5 those 6 these 7 that 8 these 9 that 10 that.

Exercise 3
1a space 1b space 2 time 3 time 4 time 5 space 6 space 7 space 8 space 9a space 9b space 10 space

Exercise 4
1 this 2 these 3 this 4 those 5 this 6 that 7 those 8 That 9 this 10 that 11 this 12 this

Exercise 5
1 that 2 that 3 this 4 This 5 that 6 this 7 that 8 those 9 these 10 that 11 this 12 that 13 that

UNIT 28
Exercise 1
1 Are there 2 There's 3 There's 4 Are there 5 There's 6 There's 7 There's 8 There's 9 Is there 10 There are

Exercise 2
1 some 2 Some 3 any 4 some 5 any 6 some, any 7 any 8 any 9 some, any, 10 some

Exercise 3
1 some 2 some 3 any 4 some 5 some 6 any 7 some 8 any 9 some 10 some 11 any 12 some

Exercise 4
1 some of 2 any of 3 all of 4 any of 5 all of 6 all of 7 some of 8 none of 9 none of 10 some of 11 any of 12 some of 13 all of 14 some of

UNIT 29
Exercise 1
1 many 2 much 3 many 4 much 5 many 6 many 7 much 8 many 9 much 10 much 11 many 12 many 13 much 14 much 15 much 16 many 17 much 18 many 19 much 20 many

Exercise 2
1 many 2 A lot of, many 3 much 4 a lot of 5 much 6 a lot of 7 much, a lot 8 a lot of 9 much 10 many 11 much 12 many 13 much 14 many/a lot 15 many

Exercise 3:
1 many 2 a lot of 3 a lot of 4 a lot of 5 much 6 a lot of 7 many 8 a lot of 9 many 10 a lot 11 a lot of 12 a lot of

13 a lot of 14 much 15 a lot of 16 a lot of 17 much 18 a lot of 19 a lot of 20 a lot of
Exercise 4
1 all of 2 many of 3 many of 4 many of 5 all of 6 a lot of 7 many of 8 a lot of 9 many of 10 a lot of
Exercise 5
1 much 2 much of 3 Many of 4 many 5 many 6 Many of 7 much 8 much of 9 much 10 much of 11 many 12 Many of 13 many 14 Many of 15 much
UNIT 30
Exercise 1
1 a few 2 a little 3 a little 4 a few 5 a little 6 a few 7 a few 8 a little 9 a little 10 a little 11 a few 12 a little 13 a little 14 a few 15 a little 16 a few 17 a few 18 a little 19 a few 20 a few 21 a little 22 a little 23 a few 24 a little 25 a few 26 a little 27 a few 28 a little 29 a few 30 a few
Exercise 2
1 a few 2 a little 3 a little 4 a few 5 a few 6 a few 7 a few 8 a few 9 a few 10 a little 11 a few 12 a little 13 a little 14 a few 15 a little
Exercise 3
1 few 2 few 3 a few 4 Few 5 A few 6 A few 7 few 8 few 9 a few 10 few 11 a few 12 a few 13 Few 14 few 15 a few
Exercise 4
1 a little 2 little 3 little 4 a little 5 little 6 little 7 little 8 little 9 a little 10 little 11 a little 12 little 13 little 14 a little 15 a little
Exercise 5
1 a few of 2 a few 3 little 4 a little of 5 a few 6 a few of 7 A few of 8 little 9 a few 10 a few
UNIT 31
Exercise 1
1 fewer 2 less 3 fewer 4 less 5 fewer 6 less 7 less 8 fewer 9 fewer, less 10 fewer
Exercise 2
1 more 2 most 3 more 4 most 5 more 6 more 7 most 8 more 9 more 10 most
Exercise 3
1 more 2 less 3a. more 3b. most 4 more 5 less 6 fewer 7 fewest 8 more 9 least 10 more/fewer
REVISION TEST 2
Units 25–26
A
1 ø 2 the 3 a 4 the 5 the 6 the 7 a 8 ø 9 ø 10 ø 11 The 12 ø 13 a 14 the
B
15 mine 16 David's/his 17 mine 18 his 19 your 20 hers
Unit 27
21 this 22 those 23 that 24 that 25 these, those
Units 28–31
A
26 any 27 None 28 some 29 any 30 None 31 no 32 any
B
33 many 34 much 35 a lot of 36 many 37 A lot of 38 much 39 A lot of 40 many of
C
41 little 42 a few 43 Few 44 a little 45 A few 46 a little
D
47 fewer/more 48 most of 49 less 50 least
UNIT 32
Exercise 1
1 She has never been to New Zealand.
2 Have you ever ridden on a horse?
3 I don't usually watch television.
4 Elephants never forget.
5 The postman always rings twice.

6 Does your cat always eat vegetables?
7 They seldom go to restaurants in the week.
8 We don't often meet Roger in town.
9 The children often play in the park.
10 Do you usually come to work by train?
11 Has she ever eaten African food?
12 We seldom stay in on Saturdays.
13 He never visits his family.
14 She doesn't usually eat lunch.
15 They often take their holiday by the sea.
16 She usually eats fruit for breakfast.
17 They often play cards together.
18 Have you ever won any money?
19 We seldom go away at Christmas.
20 She has never met my brother.
Exercise 2
1 He never goes out on Sundays.
2 Have you ever flown in a balloon?
3 Does he always travel to the United States on Concorde?
4 What do you usually do by the river in summer?
5 She's very clever. She always passes all her exams.
6 Rob always reads before going to bed.
7 I don't usually walk to work.
8 There isn't ever anyone ready to help you.
9 That wedding will never take place.
10 You can sometimes see fish jumping in this river.
11 Do you always get up at 6 o'clock?
12 We often eat out.
13 I sometimes like to go for a long walk.
14 She doesn't often get home before 8 in the evening.
15 We've never been to China.
16 Does she always go to France on holiday?
17 What does he usually do after work?
18 Anne sometimes likes to go sailing.
19 They never drink coffee.
20 When does she usually get to work?
Exercise 3
1 No, I've never seen the Queen of England.
2 Yes, I sometimes played in the park when I was a child.
3 Yes, I often go to the theatre.
4 Yes, I always do exercise at home.
5 Yes, I'll always remember you.
6 Yes, I've often been to Egypt.
7 No, I never have to wash my own clothes.
8 Yes, I always walk to school.
9 Yes, I sometimes like space films.
10 No, I can never introduce you to my boss.
11 Yes, I've often visited her parents.
12 No, I never saw that play.
13 No, I'll never go there again.
14 Yes, I sometimes eat fish.
15 No, she never learned to drive.
16 Yes, I'll often go back to Italy.
17 No, she's never seen my new house.
18 Yes, he always plays football on Saturdays.
19 Yes, she always drove fast when she was young.

20 No, I never have to stay late at work.
Exercise 4
1 Oh, John usually plays football on Saturdays.
2 Oh, Jane never cycles to work.
3 Oh, I always went to Josie's house for parties in London.
4 Oh, she'll sometimes see Roger in Paris.
5 Oh, you/I can never miss school.
6 Oh, you must always do your homework.
7 Oh, I always get up late in the morning.
8 Oh, I seldom/rarely buy new clothes.
9 Oh, Sally's never been in hospital.
10 Oh, I usually eat in restaurants.
11 I've seldom/rarely moved house.
12 She often changes her job.
13 I seldom/rarely leave work early.
14 They always went away at weekends.
15 I've never borrowed money.
16 I can often come to see you.
17 She rarely/seldom went swimming on holiday.
18 I sometimes missed my class.
19 The train usually got in late.
20 He has never changed his car.
Exercise 5
1 always 2 never 3 always 4 sometimes 5 never 6 rarely/seldom 7 usually 8 often 9 usually 10 often
UNIT 33
Exercise 1
1 better 2 fairest 3 expensive 4 most expensive 5 bad 6 worse 7 uglier 8 more beautiful 9 most beautiful 10 less 11 young 12 youngest 13 hotter 14 hottest 15 big 16 biggest 17 more important 18 most important
Exercise 2
1 hottest 2 largest 3 smaller 4 colder 5 drier 6 more 7 hotter 8 coldest 9 nearer 10 furthest
Exercise 3:
1 most expensive 2 better 3 best 4 smaller 5 worst 6 more expensive 7 larger 8 smaller 9 more expensive 10 best
Exercise 4
1 Martha is as beautiful as Annie.
2 His house is as big as mine.
3 January is as long as March.
4 April is as short as June.
5 Today is as hot as yesterday.
6 Fred is as poor as Charlie.
7 Jill is as old as her husband.
8 Cathy is as tall as John.
9 Derek is as lively as his brother.
10 Today, London is as cold as Moscow.
11 Alan is as rich as Mary.
12 You are as young as Richard.
13 John is as scared as Peter.
14 I am as angry as you.
15 This week is as wet as last week.
16 Philip is as bad as his wife.
17 Her hair is as long as mine.
18 Our dog is as big as yours.
19 Martin is as handsome as Alan.
20 I am as hungry as Anne.
Exercise 5
1 Maisie isn't as beautiful as Daisy. She's uglier.
2 Pete isn't as old as his wife. He's younger.
3 Pamela isn't as generous as Paul. She's meaner.
4 That house isn't as big as yours. It's smaller.
5 That film isn't as sad as the one you saw last week. It's happier.

6 This winter isn't as cold as last winter. It's warmer.
7 That book isn't as bad as the one you read last month. It's better.
8 This exercise isn't as difficult as exercise three. It's easier.
9 February isn't as long as September. It's shorter.
10 K2 isn't as high as Everest. It's lower.
11 John isn't as young as Peter. He's older.
12 Paris isn't as big as Tokyo. It's smaller.
13 You aren't as tall as Mary. You're shorter.
14 This play isn't as good as his first one. It's worse.
15 April isn't as warm as August. It's colder.
16 Jane isn't as tall as Catherine. She's shorter.
17 March isn't as dry as July. It's wetter.
18 Potatoes aren't as expensive as meat. They're cheaper.
19 The Channel isn't as wide as the Pacific. It's narrower.
20 This film isn't as good as his last one. It's worse.
UNIT 34
Exercise 1
1 Alan drives more carefully than John.
2 Rita sings better than Harriet.
3 George fights more aggressively than Frank.
4 This book reports better on China than yours.
5 Maisie dances in a livelier way than Anna.
6 That actress smiles in a lovelier way than her sister.
7 The cat behaves in a more friendly way than the dog.
8 When he's at home, he speaks more loudly/louder than when he's at work.
9 John swims the worst of them all.
10 Fred writes the best about paintings of this century.
11 Charles plays tennis better than Peter.
12 Alice sings more beautifully than Elaine
13 He runs fastest in the team.
14 She types carelessly.
15 Frank works harder than Tom
Exercise 2
1 faster 2 better 3 best 4 cheaply 5 most cheaply 6 badly 7 worse 8 in a livelier way 9 in the liveliest way 10 more beautifully 11 most beautifully 12 harder 13 cleverly 14 most cleverly 15 more wisely 16 most wisely 17 slowly 18 most slowly 19 angrily 20 more angrily 21 in an uglier way 22 in the ugliest way 23 quickly 24 most quickly 25 earlier 25 earliest 27 soon 28 sooner 29 far 30 furthest
Exercise 3
1 faster 2 worse 3 better 4 later 5 earlier 6 harder 7 more loudly 8 most cheerfully 9 soonest 10 more quietly 11 best 12 worst 13 more slowly 14 more soundly 15 more expensively
Exercise 4
1 David gets up as early as Mary.
2 Jane stayed at the party as late as John.
3 They sang as loudly as the pop group.
4 She greeted him as pleasantly as her sister did.

5 He came as soon as he could.
6 They ran as quickly as last year's winning team.
7 They did as little as they could.
8 We behaved as well as Tom's parents did.
9 He will leave as soon as he can.
10 They work as fast as they can.
11 They sold the books as cheaply as they could.
12 She cut the cloth as carefully as she could.
13 David works as hard as Tom.
14 May sings as beautifully as Kate.
15 The parents behaved as stupidly as their children.

Exercise 5
1 David doesn't get up as early as Mary. He gets up very late.
2 Jane didn't stay at the party as late as John. She left very early.
3 They didn't sing as loudly as the pop group. They sang very quietly.
4 She didn't greet him as pleasantly as her sister did. She greeted him very unpleasantly.
5 He didn't come as early as he could. He came very late.
6 They didn't run as quickly as last year's team. They ran very slowly.
7 They didn't do as much as they could. They did very little.
8 We didn't behave as well as Tom's parents did. We behaved very badly.
9 He won't leave as late as he can. He'll leave very early.
10 They don't work as fast as they can. They work very slowly.

Exercise 6
1 She didn't speak as boringly as the main speaker. She spoke more interestingly.
2 Jane didn't leave work as early as John. She left later.
3 Dennis doesn't play football in as dull a way as Kevin. He plays in a more lively way.
4 They didn't run as quickly as last year's team. They ran more slowly.
5 They didn't sing as loudly as the pop group. They sang more quietly.
6 Mary didn't behave as kindly as Joan. She behaved more cruelly.
7 Frank didn't behave as happily as Helen. He behaved more sadly.
8 He didn't draw as beautifully as Jane. He drew in a more ugly way.
9 Dave didn't speak as well as Tom. He spoke worse.
10 Henry didn't leave work as late as Alice. He left earlier.
11 Sally didn't speak as quietly as Nick. She spoke more loudly.
12 Mike didn't sell his car as cheaply as Rod sold his. He sold it more expensively.
13 Tim doesn't play tennis as badly as Pete. He plays better.
14 Jane's book doesn't sell as well as Mary's. It sells worse.
15 The maths teacher didn't speak as fiercely as the history teacher. He spoke more gently.

UNIT 35
Exercise 1
1 by 2 under 3 on 4 on 5 in 6 By/near 7 in 8 on 9 by 10 above 11 on
Exercise 2
1 to 2 in 3 on 4 in 5 into 6 in 7 towards

8 to 9 at 10 in
UNIT 36
Exercise 1
1 in 2 on 3 on 4 in 5 at 6 at 7 on 8 in 9 in 10 in 11 in 12 on 13 at 14 at 15 on 16 at 17 in 18 at 19 in 20 on
Exercise 2
1 on 2 in 3 in 4 on 5 in 6 at 7 at 8 at 9 on 10 in 11 in 12 in 13 On 14 in 15 on 16 on 17 in 18 in 19 at 20 in
UNIT 37
Exercise 1:
1 fast enough 2 enough money 3 hard enough 4 enough work 5 clever enough 6 warm enough 7 tall enough 8 cheap enough 9 enough rain 10 easy enough
Exercise 2
1 very 2 enough 3 too 4 very 5 too 6 too 7 too 8 too 9 very 10 too
Exercise 3
1 too 2 very 3 enough 4 very 5 too 6 enough 7 enough 8 very 9 enough 10 very

REVISION TEST 3
Unit 32
A
1 John always goes to work by bus.
2 Sally doesn't often see her friends.
3 She's sometimes in that restaurant.
4 Do you often play tennis with Mary?
5 We have seldom seen a bad play at that theatre.
6 He often loses his keys.
7 We mustn't always be late.
8 They usually spend their holidays in Britain.
9 The trains are always early.
10 Does he always come home early?
B
11 always 12 sometimes 13 seldom /rarely 14 often 15 never
Unit 33
16 most beautiful 17 better 18 older 19 worse 20 bad 21 best 22 wettest 23 taller 24 cleverest 25 bigger
Unit 34
26 fast 27 early 28 more lively/ livelier 29 hardest 30 worse 31 faster 32 better 33 hard 34 more angrily 35 more happily
Units 35–36
A
36 in 37 on 38 Under 39 In 40 out of 41 towards
B
42 on 43 at 44 in 45 at
Unit 37
46 too 47 enough 48 very 49 too 50 enough
UNIT 38
Exercise 1
1–10 that
Exercise 2
1 who 2 which 3 which 4 which 5 who 6 which 7 which 8 which 9 who 10 who
Exercise 3
1 Where is the book which was here on the table.
2 David sold me the horse which won the big race last week.
3 Mary has bought a house which used to be a shop.
4 That's the boy who took Jane's bicycle.
5 The girl who came top in the physics exam has gone to university.
6 The dog which lives near the village shop is very dangerous.
7 John wrote the letter which came

this morning.
8 Give it to the little girl who found our cat.
9 He doesn't like that film which was at the cinema last week.
10 That's the woman who came to live here last month.
Exercise 4
1 who 2 which 3 which 4 who 5 who 6 which 7 who 8 who 9 who 10 which
Exercise 5
1 who went to school with him 2 who have played with him for five years 3 who have never seen the girl before 4 who has won his heart 5 which was near his home 6 who lived in a small house 7 who was a heart surgeon 8 which was for all people in their year in the district 9 which was usually the school gym 10 who was wearing a green dress
UNIT 39
Exercise 1
1 who/whom 2 which 3 which 4 who/whom 5 who/whom 6 which 7 which 8 who/whom 9 which 10 which.
Exercise 2
1 I want to see the film Jane saw yesterday.
2 Where is the house John and Mary have just bought.
3 They don't like that girl Jimmy took to the cinema.
4 Do you know the man your dog bit?
5 I haven't read the book you bought for my birthday.
6 That's the tall woman Pamela saw in the park.
7 John's got a computer Paul wants.
8 Now Joanne's climbed the hills Dick climbed on his last holiday.
9 Let's play that game we played last night.
10 The animals ate the food we gave them.
Exercise 3
1 I want to see the film which Jane saw yesterday.
2 Where is the house which John and Mary have just bought.
3 They don't like that girl who Jimmy took to the cinema.
4 Do you know the man who your dog bit?
5 I haven't read the book which you bought for my birthday.
6 That's the tall woman who Pamela saw in the park.
7 John's got a computer which Paul wants.
8 Now Joanne's climbed the hills which Dick climbed on his last holiday.
9 Let's play that game which we played last night.
10 The animals ate the food which we gave them.
Exercise 4
1 which 2 which 3 who 4 who 5 who 6 which 7 which 8 which 9 who 10 who
Exercise 5
1 which he built himself
2 which he took from his workers
3 who the townspeople were afraid of
4 which he went to
5 who he talked to or played with
6 which his aunt owned
7 who people in the town admired
8 which he bought
9 which he owned
10 who he was at school with

Exercise 6
1 That's the chair I bought last week.
That's the chair which I bought last week.
2 The pianist you heard on the radio last night is visiting our town next week.
The pianist who you heard on the radio last night is visiting our town next week.
3 I don't like the house he lives in.
I don't like the house which he lives in.
4 The car he sold us is no good.
The car which he sold us is no good.
5 David wrote a play everybody liked.
David wrote a play which everybody liked.
6 The music you play is very old-fashioned.
The music which you play is very old-fashioned.
7 Mary sold the jewellery her husband gave her.
Mary sold the jewellery which her husband gave her.
8 The clothes he wears are very old.
The clothes which he wears are very old.
9 They didn't speak to the man the police wanted.
They didn't speak to the man who the police wanted.
10 The woman he married is very rich.
The woman who he married is very rich.
11 That's the worker the boss promoted last week.
That's the worker who the boss promoted last week.
12 The trees they cut down were very dangerous.
The trees which they cut down were very dangerous.
13 I always speak to the woman you live opposite.
I always speak to the woman who you live opposite.
14 That's a film nobody likes.
That's a film which nobody likes.
15 Her father didn't like the man she wanted to marry.
Her father didn't like the man who she wanted to marry.
16 Give me the letter John sent you.
Give me the letter which John sent you.
17 I always eat in restaurants John recommends.
I always eat in restaurants which John recommends.
18 The girl you brought to the party is going to marry my cousin.
The girl who you brought to the party is going to marry my cousin.
19 He liked the music he heard in Tuscany.
He liked the music which he heard in Tuscany.
20 I must catch the wild cat you saw in my garden.
I must catch the wild cat which you saw in my garden.
UNIT 40
Exercise 1
1 The horse whose owner is very rich.
2 The girl whose hair is long and blonde.
3 The car of which people spoke highly.

4 The actor whose wife left him.

5 The writer whose talent is very great.

6 The jewel the owner of which sold for £120,000.

7 The town the bus service of which is perfect.

8 The house the owner of which bought for £1 million.

9 The painting of which many copies were made.

10 The club, most members of which are very young.

11 The woman whose husband is a football star.

12 The tree whose red leaves are admired by everyone/the tree the red leaves of which are admired by everyone.

13 John whose photographs people liked a lot.

14 The dog whose owner is blind.

15 The school the pupils of which are very bad.

Exercise 2

1 whose **2** of which **3** of which **4** of which **5** of whom **6** of which **7** whose **8** whose **9** of which **10** of which **11** of which **12** of which **13** whose

Exercise 3

1 The students, many of whom have rich parents, work on the boats in their holidays.

2 The captains, whose boats are designed for training work, are all good teachers.

3 The drivers, most of whom were from Brazil, arrived at the track early.

4 The champion jockey, whose horse was very old, lost the big race.

5 The policeman arrested the thieves, some of whom were well-known criminals.

6 The bank manager spoke to the students, a few of whom had no money in the bank.

7 The doctor spoke kindly to the old man whose wife was very ill.

8 The woman whose son came top in the exam was very proud.

9 That's the dog whose owner doesn't feed it properly.

10 Is that the man whose daughter married a famous singer last week?

11 The girl whose new dress was torn by the cleaners was very angry.

12 The teacher told the children many of whom had no heavy coats for the cold weather to stay inside.

13 The writer whose novel won the most important prize didn't like being famous.

Exercise 4

1 MaryLou whose mother was a famous artist lives in Bombay now.

2 Give the money to the first person whose car was registered in 1998.

3 The football club of which Terry is a member is near the electricity station.

4 Shakespeare's plays, several of which are comedies, are still performed after three hundred years.

5 There are six Indian restaurants in this town, five of which are owned by the same man.

6 I don't want to read that book of which people speak very badly.

7 Daisy liked the animals whose

owners looked after them well.

8 They bought the diamond the original owner of which was the world's richest woman.

9 Those are the reporters some of whom angered the President.

10 Don't go with that group of travellers most of whom have never travelled before.

11 Let's go to meet the artist whose paintings have won many prizes.

12 I want to see the play of which the critics spoke very highly.

13 Those are our holiday photographs half of which were taken by my brother.

Exercise 5

1 the roof of which was badly damaged **2** the owner of which lived in Australia **3** whose father was very rich **4** none of which are known **5** the workers of which were unhappy **6** the managers of which were always sacking people **7** some of which his father had given him **8** many of which were very old and valuable **9** whose car John crashed **10** whose father knew the man.

UNIT 41

Exercise 1

1 He arrived on the day on which there was a circus in the town.

2 She remembered the days on which she had been happy.

3 They bought the house in which the old man died.

4 I've been back to the church in which I got married.

5 He's left the town in which he was born.

6 That was the year in which my son was born.

7 I remember the day on which I bought my first computer.

8 She's forgotten the village in which she grew up.

9 Enjoy the time in which you are young and strong.

10 You mustn't go into the rooms in which they keep their private possessions.

11 I've read the book in which the author criticizes the government.

12 She's seen the play six times in which they sing their favourite song.

13 September is the month in which I go on holiday every year.

14 That's the field in which the children play football.

15 I'd like to go back to the time in which I lived in Japan.

Exercise 2

1 That's the house where the murder happened.

2 That was the year when I met my wife.

3 Mary met David in 1996 when she was in Cairo.

4 He became President in that year when we won the World Cup.

5 Peter's working in that building where they have a lot of exhibitions.

6 I want to live on a tropical island where there's lots of sun and fruit.

7 Maisie has lived in Turkey, where she teaches English, since 1993.

8 You must plant those flowers in the spring when the ground is just right.

9 Get off the train at that station where you can see the new football stadium.

10 There's not much happening in the town where I used to live.

11 This is the desert where they broke the world land-speed record.

12 Jenny has the photograph where you'd dressed as a clown.

13 In the park there's an old hut where we used to hide when we were children.

14 I remember the day when the President was shot.

15 Jean passed her exams in the year when most people failed.

Exercise 3

1 where **2** where **3** when **4** when **5** where **6** where **7** when **8** where **9** when **10** where **11** where **12** when **13** when **14** where **15** where

Exercise 4

1 in which **2** on which **3** in which **4** in which **5** in which **6** in which **7** in which **8** in which **9** in which **10** on which **11** on which **12** in which **13** in which **14** in which **15** in which

Exercise 5:

1 when **2** where **3** where **4** where **5** when **6** where **7** where **8** when **9** where **10** where **11** where **12** when

UNIT 42

Exercise 1

1 g **2** d **3** j **4** i **5** k **6** c **7** e **8** a **9** f **10** b **11** h

Exercise 2

1 finish/have finished **2** saw **3** was **4** will be **5** arrives **6** were **7** was **8** am (I'm) **9** have **10** will have to

Exercise 3

1 was sitting **2** heard **3** were listening/listened **4** is working **5** are playing **6** was making **7** is studying **8** was living

Exercise 4

1 While they were having tea.

2 There was a loud explosion.

3 She was working in her study.

4 While they were saving things in the house.

5 He was checking the damage.

6 They were talking to the police.

7 The police were listening to John's report.

8 While they were clearing the damaged room.

9 They were clearing the damaged room.

10 She was working in her study.

Exercise 5

1 What happened while Mary and Peter were playing tennis?

2 When did the phone ring with the wrong number?

3 What was the first thing that happened while Mary was working in her study?

4 When did Peter 'phone the police?/When was there a loud explosion?

5 When did the police/firemen arrive?

6 What was the second thing that happened while they were saving things in the house?

7 When did John's wife arrive?

8 What was John doing while Mary and Peter were talking to the police?/ When his wife arrived?

9 When did the firemen leave?

10 What was the second thing that happened while they were clearing the damaged room?

UNIT 43

Exercise 1

1 spoke **2** quarrelled **3** sees **4** left **5** have had/have **6** will phone **7** has left/leaves **8** have left/leave **9** has read/reads **10** has been **11** watches **12** went **13** come/have come **14** met

15 will help

Exercise 2

1 met **2** reach **3** goes **4** will be **5** went **6** liked **7** became **8** was **9** arrive **10** will get **11** got **12** arrives **13** will begin **14** leaves **15** didn't know

Exercise 3

1 He used to see her in the park before he spoke to her.

2 David'll go to work before he goes to the football match.

3 Every day, Sally has breakfast before she listens to the radio.

4 They'll look at the house before they buy it.

5 He'll wait until the car breaks down before he sells it.

6 Mark always reads the reviews before he buys a book.

7 Mary will go to Spain before she starts her new job.

8 The painting will be finished before you come back home.

9 They'll destroy the park before they stop cutting down the trees.

10 She's determined to win the championship before she leaves school.

11 He left the party before there was the accident.

12 He'll meet you here before you leave together.

13 Robert will get his exam results before he looks for a job.

14 We'll go to the cinema before we have dinner.

15 You must finish that work before we go for a swim.

Exercise 4

1 Alan will return to work after he's got/he gets married.

2 We'll have a holiday after the summer's over.

3 John has breakfast after he swims every morning.

4 My brother left home after he took those photographs of the family.

5 Joan got to the station after the train left.

6 The rains came after there was a long, dry summer.

7 She saw the film after she read the book.

8 They lived in Istanbul after the lived in Rome.

9 She arrived after he left for work.

10 I'll start painting the house after I go/I've been for a walk.

11 Robert wrote Jane a letter after he heard the news.

12 Alice will get ready for the party after she has done the shopping.

13 David will try to sell the painting after he has restored it.

14 We'll tell everyone the news after they've finished dinner.

15 Susan burnt Tom's books after he left her.

Exercise 5

1 Before **2** after **3** after **4** before **5** after **6** before **7** after **8** after **9** before **10** before.

UNIT 44

Exercise 1

1 c **2** i **3** f **4** g **5** a **6** e **7** j **8** b **9** k **10** h **11** d

Exercise 2

1 I gave him some money so that/in order that he can buy some food.

2 She read her baby son a story so that/in order that he would go to sleep.

3 Jane has saved a lot of money so that/in order that her parents have a good holiday.

4 He gave the paintings to the museum so that/in order that everyone can see them.
5 She's putting the fire on so that/in order that the guests will be warm.
6 We'll go to the airport early so that/in order that you won't miss your flight.
7 I'll phone so that/in order that you know I arrived safely.
8 He bought her an expensive ring so that/in order that she would marry him.
9 Lydia gave Sam the book so that/in order that he studied for his exam.
10 She always pants a lot of flowers so that/in order that the garden looks lovely.

Exercise 3
1 She drove very fast to/in order to arrive early.
2 They bought expensive seats for the play to/in order to get good seats.
3 He read the book three times to/in order to be certain of the murderer.
4 She always goes to Zurich in May to/in order to have Swiss asparagus.
5 He came early in order not to miss the beginning of the game.
6 He's going to Germany to/in order to see Eva, his future wife.
7 They've bought a house near the sea to/in order to go sailing.
8 He plays his music loudly to/in order to annoy his neighbours.
9 I stayed at the party late in order not to go home with Mary.
10 She sold her jewels to/in order to get some money.

Exercise 4
1 to 2 to 3 so that 4 to 5 so that 6 to 7 so that 8 so that 9 to 10 so that 9 to 10 so that

Exercise 5
1 So that the children could cross the road safely.
2 To complain of the bad service.
3 To be at my brother's wedding.
4 So that the boss will give her a better job.
5 In order not to be there in the tourist season.
6 In order not to lose these important documents.
7 To annoy the neighbours.
8 So that he won't borrow mine.
9 So that everyone can see it easily.
10 To celebrate my good exam results.

UNIT 45
Exercise 1a
1 e 2 h 3 b 4 f 5 i 6 a 7 j 8 k 9 d 10 c 11 g
Exercise 1b
1 B 2 C 3 B 4 B 5 B 6 A 7 B 8 A 9 B 10 A 11 B
Exercise 2
1 John comes home late these days because he's unhappy at home.
2 I saw that film twice because the actress is very good.
3 I was very polite to him because he will be my boss next month.
4 You'll have to go without me because I'm not ready yet.
5 The holiday is costing a lot of money because you want to stay in the best hotel.
6 I'm going to India next month because I've got some work there.
7 They can't sell that house because

it's in a bad position.
8 You should do more exercise because you're too fat.
9 I'm going home early because I'm tired.
10 The train's delayed because there were cows on the line.
11 Paul is studying astronomy because he wants to go to the moon.
12 They have a very big dog because it frightens off burglars
13 He climbed through the window because he lost his keys.
14 Simon's got two jobs because he needs the money.
15 Pauline is studying French because she wants to marry Pierre.

REVISION TEST 4
Units 38–39
1 John owns that car which was stolen.
2 Mary's friend who lives in the large house on the hill is very rich.
3 The park which closes at 6 o'clock is very dangerous at night.
4 Give me the book which/ø Mary gave you.
5 I can't buy the radio which/ø I want.
6 The woman who lives in that house is very old.
7 He likes the white houses which are in southern Spain.
8 It's a very attractive place which/ø I bought last year.
9 He caught the train which is the quickest to London.
10 The boy climbed the tree which is the tallest in the park.
11 The boy who is very strong climbed to the top of the tree.
12 They don't like that man who's going to be their teacher.
13 I thought that exercise which/ø the teacher us was very difficult.
14 The journey you planned was boring.
15 The holiday you missed was lovely.

Units 40–41
A
16 whose 17 of whom 18 of which 19 whose 20 whose 21 whose 22 of which 23 of which 24 of which
B
25 when 26 when 27 where 28 where 29 where 30 when 31 when 32 where
Units 42–43
33 am 34 was sitting 35 'll get 36 'm studying 37 have seen 38 read 39 has 40 visited
Unit 44
41 He's working hard now to get a better job.
42 David stayed at home so that Jane could go to the play.
43 He put the picture in the study so that everyone could see it.
44 She does exercise every day to keep fit.
45 He caught the early train to meet Joan for lunch.
Unit 45
46 is 47 was 48 will become 49 will become 50 is
EXIT TEST
Units 1–11
1 goes 2 lives 3 is writing 4 is your daughter studying 5 play, 'm walking 6 lives, is staying 7 goes 8 is acting 9 doesn't like 10 did you do 11 saw 12 didn't do 13 were walking

14 wasn't talking 15 was reading, didn't finish 16 was listening, phoned 17 Did you go 18 used to cycle/cycled 19 didn't go 20 have lived 21 Have you seen 22 hasn't gone/hasn't been 23 Have you ever been 24 went 25 Have you seen 26 I've never been 27 went 28 'll be 29 'll see 30 'll win/are going to win 31 leaves 32 'm seeing
Units 12–17
A
33 must 34 should 35 will be able to 36 need 37 can/could 38 can 39 must 40 have to 41 should 42 mustn't 43 could/may/might 44 can't/are unable to
B
45 Can 46 can't 47 could 48 may not 49 can 50 must
UNIT 18
51 So is 52 Nor/neither did 53 So must 54 Nor/neither should
Units 19–20
55 wants 56 sees, talks 57 'll be 58 lived 59 saw, followed 60 'll be, cut
Unit 21
61 Those trees were planted by my uncle.
62 A best-selling novel has been written by my friend.
63 My garden was destroyed by those dogs.
Units 22–23
64 The secretary told Richard the doctor would see him on Wednesday.
65 John asked Daisy where Mary had put his book.
66 The policeman asked Mrs Brown if Mr Brown was at home.
67 David's mother told him not to bring the cat in.
Unit 24
68 can you 69 didn't you 70 don't they
Unit 25
71 a 72 no article 73 the/a 74 the 75 the 76 The 77 no article 78 a 79 a 80 The 81 The 82 The 83 a 84 the
Units 26–27
85 That, mine 86 This, Richard's 87 those, your 88 the farmer's
Unit 28
89 some 90 any 91 any 92 no
Units 29–30
93 much 94 many 95 a lot 96 few 97 little
Unit 31
98 most 99 Fewer 100 less
Unit 32
101 The lions always gathered near the lake at five o'clock.
102 You rarely/seldom see a good film nowadays.
Units 33–34
103 oldest 104 harder 105 heavier 106 most beautifully
Units 35–36
107 at 108 in 109 on 110 in
Unit 37
111 very 112 too 113 enough
Units 38–40
114 Books which were written thirty years ago don't interest.
115 The prize went to the actor who won it last year.
116 I didn't like the film which I saw last week.
117 Next week he'll visit his aunt who lives in Oxford.
118 That's the man whose car was stolen.
119 He's a member of the city administration, the chairman of which is an unpleasant man.

Unit 41
120 when 121 where 122 when 123 where
Units 42–43
124 was sitting 125 arrive 126 gets 127 sees/has seen
Units 44–45
128 Paul worked hard to get a better job.
129 Mary studied hard so that her father would be proud of her.
130 The dog ran away because the man chased it with a stick.

13 Later on he found .... ten pence!
14 I heard .... dog barking all last night.
15 It was in .... house over the road.

3   Write the correct article

Write the correct article (the, a, an, or no article). The first one has been done for you.

Dear Tom,

We had *a* lovely holiday last month. We went to (**1**) ..... island in Greece. David preferred to go to (**2**) ..... beach, but I liked climbing in (**3**) ..... hills some days. David said he saw (**4**) ..... dolphin, but Anne says it was (**5**) ..... shark. Anne was right. I saw (**6**) ..... shark myself. There wasn't much to do in (**7**) ..... evenings, but there was (**8**) ..... very good restaurant. (**9**) ..... restaurant was at (**10**) ..... beach, and on Tuesdays, Thursdays and Saturdays, there was (**11**) ..... disco on (**12**) ..... beach. (**13**) ..... disco was very good and we met (**14**) ..... lot of young people there. I think Anne found (**15**) ..... new boy-friend. David and I didn't have much luck with (**16**) ..... girls. Anne's boy-friend writes to Anne every day. He's Swedish, so they won't be able to see each other very often. I don't think her parents are very happy that she is getting (**17**) ..... letters from Sweden. They want to know more about him.

Let me know about your holiday.

All good wishes,
Andy

---

4   Write the correct article

Write the correct article (the, a, an, or no article) in this verse.

THE OWL AND THE PUSSY-CAT
(**1**)..... Owl and (**2**)..... Pussy-cat went to sea
In (**3**)..... beautiful pea-green boat,
They took some honey, and plenty of (**4**)..... money,
Wrapped up in (**5**)..... five-pound note.
(**6**)..... Owl looked up to (**7**)..... stars above,
And sang to (**8**)..... small guitar,
'O lovely Pussy! O Pussy, my love,
What (**9**)..... beautiful Pussy you are,
You are,
You are!
What (**10**)..... beautiful Pussy you are!'

5   Choose the use

Read the sentences, and choose which use of the (A–E) each shows.

A when you know the person or thing you mean
B when you have talked about the person or thing before
C when the thing or person is unique
D for countries that are a lot of states
E for names of rivers, ranges of mountains
Example:
The Queen of England lives in London. $\boxed{C}$

1   They built **the** Eiffel Tower in 1897.   □
2   I want to see **the** man who lives in **the** red house.   □ □
3   **The** sun rises in **the** east.   □ □
4   He ordered flowers for her birthday, but **the** flowers arrived late.   □
5   We've just had a holiday on **the** Danube.   □
6   There was an old person of Ems
Who casually fell in **the** Thames ...   □
7   J was a jackdaw
Who hopped up and down
In **the** principal street,
Of a neighbouring town.   □
        J!
All through **the** town.   □
8   Lancaster is a small city in **the** north-west of England.   □
9   **The** Romans built a fortress on **the** top of a hill by **the** River Lune.   □ □
10   **The** Normans built a castle there.   □
11   **The** castle is now used as a prison and a court.   □
12   **The** prison is very old.   □
13   **The** court is only used for small crimes now.   □
14   Lancaster was **the** capital city of Lancashire until 1974.   □
15   **The** poet, Robert Southey, said **the** view from **the** river to **the** castle was **the** most beautiful in Britain.   □ □ □ □

Possessive Pronouns and Genitives

my, mine, your, yours, David's

FORM AND USE

Look at these statements. They are both about what belongs to which person.
That's my book. And that pen's mine.
That book's yours. And that's your pen.
There are two ways to show that something belongs to you.

POSSESSIVE ADJECTIVE
That's my/your/our/his/her/its/their favourite place.

POSSESSIVE PRONOUN
That car's mine/yours/ours/his/hers/theirs.
Notes:
1 The possessive pronoun is formed by adding *s* to the possessive adjective, except in the case of *his*, which already ends in *s*, and *mine*.
2 There is no possessive pronoun for *its*, which usually refers to an animal.
3 It's = It is, but *its* shows possession. There is no apostrophe for the possessive adjective.

1 Complete the chart

PERSON	POSSESSIVE ADJECTIVE	POSSESSIVE PRONOUN
I		
You		
He		
She		
It		
We		
They		

2 Complete the sentences

Complete the sentences with the correct possessive adjective.
Example:
He's taken *his* car to the garage.

1 John gave .... bicycle to his brother.
2 That's .... book. I bought it last week.
3 Mary and John spent .... holiday in The Gambia.
4 Malcolm lost .... job after he quarrelled with the boss.
5 All animals protect .... babies.
6 Jane's lost .... watch.
7 Greta was proud of .... garden.
8 William got very angry with .... students.
9 That biscuit was very hard. I've broken .... tooth.

10 They're .... chocolates. John gave them to you.
11 We gave .... old car away.
12 He trained in France. .... cooking is excellent.
13 This is .... new dog. We got him last week.
14 Sarah still hasn't got .... watch back.
15 William and Jane gave me .... cat to look after when they went away.

3 Rewrite the sentences

Rewrite the sentences using a possessive pronoun.
Example:
That book belongs to me. *That book's mine.*
Mary owns that house. *That house is hers.*

1 That car belongs to John. ....
2 Those shoes belong to Mary. ....
3 Those dirty clothes belong to you. ....
4 The farmer owns the fields behind our house. ....
5 That house over there belongs to the President. ....
6 The boat over there belongs to my brother. ....
7 Mr Davis owns this company. ....
8 My parents own that restaurant. ....
9 They own that furniture. ....
10 That football belongs to James. ....
11 We own that boat. ....
12 Those cars over there belong to my parents. ....
13 She owns all the land round here ....
14 That book belongs to us. ....
15 He owns those shops in the High Street. ....

GENITIVES

When we are talking about a person, e.g. David, we add an apostrophe (') and *s* to the name
That book belongs to David.
That's David's book.
or
That book's David's.
When we are talking about more than one person, e.g. his parents, or the name ends in *s*, we add only an apostrophe
That house belongs to his parents.
That's his parents' house.
or
That house is his parents'.
That book belongs to David Davis.
That's David Davis' book.

or
That book's David Davis'.
We can also use this form for institutions.
That land belongs to the school.
It's the school's land.
or
That land is the school's.
Note:
Be careful not confuse the meaning of apostrophe *s* ('s). It is either the short form of *is* or *has*,
David's late. (David is late).
David's finished. (David has finished.)
or it shows possession
David's car, the car is David's.

---

4 Rewrite the sentences

Rewrite the sentences, the possessive form of the name or the noun.
Example:
That belongs to John. ....
It's John's car. or *That car's John's.*

1 Those flowers belong to Mary. .... or
....

2 That television belongs to the college. ....
or ....

3 Those computers belong to the Institute.
.... or ....

4 The football club belongs to the members.
.... or ....

5 That typewriter belongs to Alice. .... or
....

6 That shop belongs to my father. .... or
....

7 This land belongs to the President. .... or
....

8 That castle belongs to Dracula. .... or
....

9 Those cows belong to the farmer. .... or
....

10 That coat belongs to the Matthew. .... or
....

5 Complete the dialogue

Complete the dialogue below with a possessive adjective or a possessive pronoun. The first one has been done for you.

John: Is this *your* purse with all this money?
Pamela: No, it's not *mine*. I thought it was (**1**) ....
John: No, I've got (**2**) .... in my pocket. Here. Perhaps it belongs to Daisy.
Pamela: If it's (**3**) ...., she'll be very worried. She's gone shopping.
John: Well, the purse looks like (**4**) ....
Pamela: No, it doesn't. This purse is black. Daisy doesn't have a black purse.
John: Then who does the purse belong to? Mary?
Pamela: No, it's not (**5**) .... (**6**) .... purse is blue.
John: What about Alan? He has a purse, and (**7**) .... is black.
Pamela: Where is he now? Is he working at (**8**) .... desk?
John: No. He's gone with Sally to (**9**) .... favourite restaurant.
Pamela: But he'll have no money, if this purse and money are (**10**) ....
John: He'll have to wash the dishes after the meal!

FORM AND USE

DEMONSTRATIVES

1   Put *this/that* before singular nouns
this table, *that house*, *this furniture*,
that information

2   Put *these/those* before plural nouns
these cars, *those trains*

3   Use demonstratives to show which things you are talking about, and to say whether they are near or far from your point of view.
This building is very old.
That man over there is very rich.
I'd like one kilo of these potatoes and half a kilo of those carrots.

4   Use *this* for time which is in the present and near future.
this year, *this month*, *this week*
When we say *this* + time, we mean the current ones. For days of the week, we mean the next one coming.
this Friday

5   Use *that* for time which is in the past, and for activities in the past.
yesterday, *last month*

1   Complete the sentences

Complete the sentences using this, that, these *or* those.

1   Put (a) .... chairs here round (b) .... tables over there.

2   I went to the theatre last Saturday but .... Saturday, I'll stay at home.

3   I didn't like .... pudding yesterday.

4   We're going to have fish for dinner .... evening.

5   .... boy over there in the corner is the one who started the fight.

6   .... diamond in the glass cabinet over there is worth $7 million.

7   Have you seen .... lovely pictures in the shop in the High Street.

8   Give me .... book on the table behind you, please.

9   I want all the chairs in (a) .... room painted blue, and (b) .... in the garden room painted red.

10   Jeffrey doesn't like .... man standing by the door.

2   Complete the dialogue

Complete the dialogue with this, that, these *or* those.

Anne: (**1**) .... box here is mine, and (**2**) .... one over there is yours.

Bob: But (**3**) .... one is smaller than yours.

Anne: I know, but (**4**) .... box will be easier to carry.

Bob: But I've got to put all (**5**) .... books in my room into it. It won't be big enough.

Anne: What about me? I've got all (**6**) .... books here.

Bob: Then there's (**7**) .... typewriter on my desk.

Anne: Well, I've got all (**8**) .... important papers here. I must take them all.

Bob: Why can't I have (**9**) .... box? And I'll find you another one.

Anne: Oh, all right. But then I want (**10**) .... picture in the hall.

Bob: That's not fair.

3 Tick time or space

Look at exercise 1 again and tick (✔) whether this, that, these *or* those *has been used in a time reference or a space reference.*

	Space	Time
1a	☐	☐
1b	☐	☐
2	☐	☐
3	☐	☐
4	☐	☐
5	☐	☐
6	☐	☐
7	☐	☐
8	☐	☐
9a	☐	☐
9b	☐	☐
10	☐	☐

4 Complete the commentary

Complete the commentary with this, that, these *or* those.

'You must be very quiet in (**1**) .... room, because (**2**) .... walls are very thin and (**3**) .... door doesn't close so that (**4**) .... people in the next room can hear everything you say or do. Now you can come in (**5**) .... Tuesday and Thursday, but next week will be different. On (**6**) .... Tuesday, we'll need the room for a meeting. The meeting will disturb (**7**) .... people next door, but we haven't got another room unfortunately. (**8**) .... cupboard over there in the corner is always locked, but you can use (**9**) .... desk here to put some things in. And you can use (**10**) .... coat-stand in the hall for your coats. I think (**11**) .... room is better than the one you looked at (**12**) .... morning.'

5 Complete the dialogue

Complete the dialogue with this, that, these *or* those. *Look at the picture below for the places.*

Ted:	I think the prisoner is in (**1**) .... house behind (**2**) .... wood.
Ron:	One kilometre away.
Ted:	Yes. Now we can hide in (**3**) .... barn. (**4**) .... farm belongs to a friend of mine.
Ron:	When did you last see the prisoner?
Ted:	Three weeks ago. Do you remember the day of the world football match? The prisoner disappeared on (**5**) .... day.
Ron:	Is he in danger? Must we rescue him quickly?
Ted:	Very quickly. Today's Wednesday. We must do it before (**6**) .... Friday.
Ted:	The day after tomorrow. It'll be dangerous crossing (**7**) .... river.
Ted:	Yes. And we must do it quietly. We mustn't worry (**8**) .... cows.
Ron:	Or (**9**) .... sheep.
Ted:	Do you see (**10**) .... tower by the river?
Ron:	Yes.
Ted:	We've got a friend in there. We contact him by pulling (**11**) .... flag up and down.
Ron:	What will he do?
Ted:	He'll help us.
Ron:	How?
Ted:	I don't know. But he knows a way through (**12**) .... wood to (**13**) .... house.

USE

1 Use *some* with positive statements
There's some tea in the cupboard.
There are some clean plates on the table.
Note:
Some is used with countable and uncountable nouns.
2 Use *any, no* with negative statements
She hasn't got any money.
He didn't buy any apples.
We use *no* when we are talking about possessing
She's got no money.
or indicating something
There are no apples in that shop today.
Note:
Any and *no* are used with countable and uncountable nouns.

3 Use *any* with questions
Have you got any milk?
Are there any oranges in that shop?
Note:
When you are offering something or expect the answer to be *yes*, you can use *some* for questions
Would you like some tea?
4 There is no need to repeat the noun
*Could you lend me some **milk**?*
*I'm sorry, I haven't got **any**.*
(We understand that the second speaker is referring to milk.)
Note:
For general use, we use *somebody/someone, anybody/anyone, something/anything*.

1 Complete the sentences

Complete the sentences with there is, there are, is there *or* are there.
Example:
Is there any meat in the fridge?
There are some nice flowers in that shop.

1 .... any shops open today?
2 .... some food on the table.
3 .... no money for holidays this year.
4 .... any postcards of the town?
5 .... some information about Thailand in that book.
6 .... no French wine in the shops here.
7 .... some French cheese.
8 .... some violence in that film.
9 .... any homework tonight?
10 .... no trees in that street.

2 Fill in the gaps

Fill in the gaps in the sentences with some *or* any.
Examples:
Would you like *some* tea?
I didn't get *any* letters today.

1 Could I have .... milk, please?
2 .... people don't eat meat.
3 We didn't have .... snow in England last year.
4 Would you like .... cake?
5 They haven't sold .... tickets for the concert.

6 We looked at .... pictures, but we didn't buy ....
7 Have you got .... chocolate?
8 He heard a noise, but he couldn't see .... body.
9 They've given .... money to the hospital and .... to the school, but they didn't give .... to the museum.
10 She had .... adventures when she was young, before she got married.

3 Complete the dialogue

John and Sarah are preparing to go on holiday in India. Complete the dialogue with some, any. *The first one has been done for you.*

Sarah: Have you got *any* Indian money?
John: No. But I've got **(1)** .... travellers' cheques.
Sarah: Then we can get **(2)** .... money at the airport.
John: Yes. I couldn't buy **(3)** .... sun lotion yesterday. There was none in the shops at all.
Sarah: Don't worry. I've got **(4)** ....
John: And what about insect spray?
Sarah: I've got a little. But you'll have to buy **(5)** .... yourself.
John: Did you get **(6)** .... information about the hotel?
Sarah: A little. There was **(7)** .... in your guide book.

John: Has there been (**8**) .... news about the flight?

Sarah: No! Why?

John: (**9**) .... flights are delayed.

Sarah: They only tell you that at the airport. Now, I've got (**10**) .... books for the holiday.

John: But you haven't got (**11**) .... newspapers or magazines.

Sarah: We can buy (**12**) .... at the airport. Now let's go or we'll be late.

SOME/ANY/NO + OF + DETERMINER

When there is a determiner (*the*, *his*, *her*, *our*, *my*, *your*, *this*, *that*, etc.) before the noun, we put *of* after *some* or *any*. And instead of *no*, we use *none*.
Some of the students were late for the exam.
Have you seen **any of the** films at the cinemas this week?

None of his friends came to the party.

We also use *all* in this way
All of **his** friends came to the party.

---

4   **Complete the sentences**

Look at the rule box above, then do this exercise.
The table below shows the results in the sports events for some students at the college. They all took part in different age-groups. Complete the sentences with all of, some of, any of *or* none of.

	100m	200m	1000m	Hurdles	Long jump	High jump
Bill (11–13)	won	won	won	lost	won	lost
Andy (17–19)	lost	lost	lost	lost	lost	lost
Sarah (13–15)	won	won	won	won	won	won
Hannah (15–17)	lost	won	lost	won	won	lost

Example:
Did Bill win *any of* his events?

1   Bill lost .... his events.
2   Did Andy win .... his events?
3   No, he lost .... his events.
4   Andy wasn't good at .... the events.
5   Sarah won .... her events.
6   She was good at .... the events.
7   Hannah lost .... her events.

8   Andy won .... his events.
9   Sarah lost .... her events.
10 Hannah won .... her events.
11 Did Bill lose .... his events?
12 Hannah was bad at .... the events?
13 Andy was bad at .... the events.
14 Hannah was good at .... the events.

UNIT 29 Quantity 2: *much / many / a lot of*

USE

1 Write *much* or *many*

1 .... books
2 .... coffee
3 .... films
4 .... money
5 .... vegetables
6 .... houses
7 .... food
8 .... sheep
9 .... noise
10 .... fruit
11 .... flowers
12 .... children
13 .... furniture
14 .... information
15 .... meat
16 .... cars
17 .... bread
18 .... people
19 .... light
20 .... chairs

2 Complete the sentences

Complete the sentences with much, many, a lot of *or* a lot.

1 There aren't .... people at the meeting.
2 .... children came to the party, but not .... liked it.
3 There isn't .... air in here. Open a window.
4 He moved house, because there was .... noise in the neighbourhood.
5 She always went to the office early, but she didn't do .... work.
6 They enjoyed themselves and had .... fun on the holiday.
7 Has the President got .... power? Oh, yes. He's got ....
8 They spent .... time preparing for the exam.
9 Do you eat .... fruit? It's very good for you.
10 Did you see .... elephants, when you visited the game park in Tanzania?
11 I didn't have .... money to spend when I was a student, but Jane had ....
12 We haven't go .... flowers in the garden this year.
13 There hasn't been .... rain.
14 I've had .... holidays in Australia, and Jim's had ...., too.
15 Do you have .... brothers and sisters?

3 Complete the dialogue

Sarah is telling her friend, Anne, about her holiday in India. Complete the dialogue with many, much *or* a lot of. *The first one has been done for you.*

Anne: Did you see *many* elephants?
Sarah: No, we didn't see (**1**) ...., but we saw (**2**) .... cows. They are often in the street. And there are always (**3**) .... cars in the streets, so there was (**4**) .... confusion.
Anne: Did you eat (**5**) .... Indian food?
Sarah: We ate (**6**) .... Indian food. It's very good for you.
Anne: How (**7**) .... places did you visit?
Sarah: We travelled all over the South. We saw (**8**) .... temples. They were very interesting. And one day we visited a crocodile farm.
Anne: Were there (**9**) .... crocodiles there?
Sarah: There were (**10**) .... It was the first time I saw a crocodile.
Anne: I suppose there were (**11**) .... tourists there.

Sarah: Yes. But there were also **(12)** .... Indians. Indians like to visit **(13)** .... the famous places in their country.

Anne: Did you hear **(14)** .... news about Britain while you were there?

Sarah: Yes. But everyday, we bought an Indian newspaper, so we read **(15)** .... news about India. And we learned **(16)** .... Indian customs.

Anne: Was there **(17)** .... sun? You're not very brown.

Sarah: We didn't sunbathe. Also it was the monsoon season, so there was **(18)** .... rain.

Anne: I've read **(19)** .... books about India. I'd like to go there.

Sarah: You must go. There are **(20)** .... interesting things to see and do there.

MUCH/MANY + OF + DETERMINER
When there is a determiner (*the*, *his*, *her*, *our*, *my*, *your*, *this*, *that*, etc.) before the noun, we put *of* after *much* or *many*.
Were **many of the** students late for the exam?
I haven't read **many of his** books.
Has she given away **much of her** money?
They didn't like **much of the** music at the concert.

---

4 Complete the sentences

Six pop groups have visited the town. Bill, Andy, Sarah and Hannah went to some of the concerts. The table below shows how many concerts they went to and how many they enjoyed and how many they didn't enjoy. Complete the sentences below with all of, many of, much *or* a lot of.

	concerts	enjoyed	didn't enjoy
Bill	6	2	4
Andy	3	3	0
Sarah	4	1	3
Hannah	5	4	1

Example:
Sarah didn't enjoy *many of* the concerts she went to.

1 Bill attended .... the concerts.
2 But he didn't enjoy .... them.

3 Did Andy go to .... the concerts?
4 No, he didn't go to .... them.
5 But he enjoyed .... the concerts he went to.
6 Sarah went to .... the concerts.
7 Did Hannah go to .... the concerts?
8 Yes, she went to .... them.
9 And did she enjoy .... the concerts?
10 Yes, she enjoyed .... the concerts she went to.

5 Complete the sentences

Complete the sentences with much, many, much of *or* many of

Example:
.... the people haven't arrived yet.
Many of the people haven't arrived yet.
I didn't see .... people at the game.
I didn't see *many* people at the game.

1 John hasn't got .... furniture in his house.
2 He bought .... the furniture in a second-hand shop.
3 .... his friends have lent him some furniture.
4 There aren't .... parks in the city.
5 Although he works in a cinema, Robert hasn't seen .... films this year.
6 .... the films are too violent for him.
7 He doesn't like .... violence in films.
8 He spends .... his time watching romantic video films.
9 The thieves didn't take .... jewellery from the house.
10 In any case, ... the jewellery wasn't real.
11 There are often .... fires in the forest when the weather is dry.
12 .... the fires are started by children playing with matches.
13 I didn't take .... photographs on holiday.
14 .... my photographs don't come out well.
15 There isn't .... light in this room. The windows are too small.

USE

1 *few* = not many (with countable nouns)
little = not much (with uncountable nouns)
2 We use *a few/a little,* when we are positive. It is better than we expected.
There were a few people for the meeting.
(I didn't expect anybody to come.)
There's a little coffee left.
(I thought it was finished.)
3 We use *few/little,* when we are negative. It is worse than we expected.

There were few people at the meeting
(I expected more.)
There's little coffee left.
(We should have bought some more.)
Notes:
1 When there is *only* in the sentence, we usually use *a few* or *a little.*
2 After *very* or *too* and before *enough,* we use *few* or *little* without *a.*

1   Write *a few* or *a little*

1	.... oranges	2	.... water
3	.... butter	4	.... eggs
5	.... paper	6	.... newspapers
7	.... banks	8	.... cheese
9	.... work	10	.... air
11	.... hours	12	.... coffee
13	.... news	14	.... cigarettes
15	.... beauty	16	.... languages
17	.... cars	18	.... money
19	.... people	20	.... clothes
21	.... tea	22	.... bread
23	.... holidays	24	.... rice
25	.... years	26	.... pain
27	.... cakes	28	.... sugar
29	.... cups	30	.... cats

2   Complete the sentences

Complete the sentences with a few *or* a little.
Example:
He smokes *a few* cigarettes each day, but not many.

1 David has bought .... new clothes this year, but not many.
2 Mr and Mrs Hunter have .... money, but not enough to buy a new car.
3 There was .... noise from the trains, but it didn't disturb me.
4 He's got .... famous paintings, but not many for such a rich man.
5 Although he's travelled a lot, he's only visited .... countries.
6 The farmer's only got .... sheep now, because he wants to retire soon.
7 There are only .... pieces of furniture left, as the shop is closing next week.

8 Jane sold only .... pieces of jewellery, because she needed some money.
9 Rita lost .... marks in the exam, because she arrived late.
10 There's .... tea left if you want some.
11 She invited .... friends over for dinner.
12 We had .... rain this morning, but this afternoon it's fine.
13 I'd like some vegetables, please, but I'll only have .... meat.
14 We took .... warm clothes with us on holiday, but we didn't need them.
15 There was a terrible storm last night, but it caused only .... damage.

3   Complete the sentences

Complete the sentences with few *or* a few.
Examples:
There were *few* people at the game. We expected more.
There were *a few* people at the game. More than I expected.

1 There are .... tickets left for the concert. It's very popular.
2 He reads .... books. He prefers magazines.
3 There are .... tickets left for the concert. They haven't sold them all yet.
4 .... children like that teacher. He's very unpopular.
5 .... children play in the children's park, although it's very new.
6 .... people have been to the exhibition, although it's not well known.
7 I've bought .... vegetables, because I don't like them.
8 He had .... friends, because he was so unkind.

9 I've bought .... books. They were selling them cheaply.

10 I've visited .... countries. I don't like travelling.

11 Although it was very late, the supermarket had ..... loaves of bread left.

12 I sent out lots of invitations, but only .... people came.

13 .... teenagers really want to go on holiday with their parents.

14 There are .... pandas left in China now. We need to do something quickly.

15 I think we've got .... eggs left. I'll look in the fridge.

4 Complete the sentences

Complete the sentences with little *or* a little.

Example:

There was *little* interest in the game. Very few people came.

There was *a little* interest in the game. More people came than I expected.

1 I got .... money from my aunt. I didn't think I would get any.

2 She's got .... chance of passing the exam. She hasn't done any work for it.

3 He does .... work at home. He's very lazy.

4 She takes .... interest in the cinema, but she prefers the theatre.

5 There is .... time before the train leaves, so you don't have to hurry.

6 Hurry up! There's .... time before the bus comes.

7 He's saved .... money at all. He spends everything he earns.

8 There's .... chance of getting tickets for the game. It's very popular.

9 There's .... milk left, but I'll get some more.

10 There's .... food in the cupboard. Who's been eating everything?

11 I've had .... practice at decorating, so I'll try to help.

12 He really had .... knowledge of gardening, and did a lot of damage to my garden!

13 The earthquake was very serious. There's .... hope of finding any survivors.

14 All you need is .... knowledge of the language to enjoy a holiday abroad.

15 She had .... money to invest, and made herself very rich.

5 Complete the dialogue

Jane and Rosie have not met for a long time. Complete the dialogue with a word or phrase from the box. The first one is done for you.

a few   a few of   few   few of   a little   a little of
little   little of

Jane: Hullo, Rosie. What are you doing here? I haven't seen you for a long time.

Rosie: But you know I live only *a few* streets away. Have you been to the film festival this year? It wasn't popular. There were *few* people there.

Jane: I'm not surprised. I saw (**1**) .... the films at the festival. The tickets were very expensive.

Rosie: That's a pity. It was a good festival There were only (**2**) .... films I didn't like.

Jane: I have (**3**) .... money these days. I'm saving to buy a car.

Rosie: But you should spend (**4**) .... that money on things you enjoy.

Jane: I buy (**5**) .... books and I've seen (**6**) .... the games at the stadium.

Rosie: That's good. You don't spend all your time alone at home. (**7**) .... your friends want to see you.

Jane: Thank you. But I have very (**8**) .... time now. My job is very busy.

Rosie: But there are (**9**) .... days when you don't work, aren't there?

Jane: Yes. You're right. I have to see (**10**) .... friends again.

UNIT 31 Quantity 4: *Comparisons*

more / most; *less / least*; *fewer / fewest*

USE

1 *more* and *most*
More is the comparative form of *much* and *many*.
I drink more tea than I used to.
Most is the superlative form of *much* and *many*.
In the north of the country, they get the most rain.
2 *less* and *least*
Less is the comparative form of *little*.
Least is the superlative form of *little*.
3 *fewer* and *fewest*
Fewer is the comparative form of *few*.

Fewest is the superlative form of *few*.
Note:
Fewer and *fewest* are seldom used now. *Less* and *least* are often used for both countable and uncountable nouns.
All these words are also used as pronouns.
He was paid more than I was.
(*He was paid more money than I was.*)

---

1 Complete the sentences

Complete the sentences with less *or* fewer.
Example:
There are *fewer* people here today than there were yesterday.

1 You've got .... books than I have.
2 That's too much. You should use .... sugar.
3 We must save money. You should make .... phone calls.
4 I earned .... money this month but I thought I worked harder.
5 That house is cheaper because it has .... rooms than this one.
6 You should eat .... meat, but more vegetables.
7 He's too fat, so he's trying to eat ....
8 Next time, buy .... apples. We don't eat a lot.
9 They are employing .... people, because there is .... work there now.
10 This room is too full. You want .... chairs in here. It's difficult to move around.

2 Complete the sentences

Complete the sentences with more *or* most.
Example:
He gets *more* money than I do.
But she gets the *most*.
1 They eat .... fish than they used to.
2 Mary and Jean have a lot of shoes, but Alice has the ....
3 The British drink .... wine these days.
4 You get the .... information on the ten o'clock news.
5 These new motorbikes make .... noise than the old ones.

6 Young people enjoy dancing .... now.
7 Among his brothers and sisters, John has read the ....
8 Jane has won .... prizes than anyone else in her school.
9 Richard has .... money than he knows what to do with.
10 Cathy takes the .... holidays in our group.

3 Complete the sentences

Complete the sentences with fewer, fewest, less, least, more, *or* most.

1 You haven't got much food there. Do you want ....?
2 You see too much television. You should watch ....
3 John did well in the game, but Peter scored .... points, and David scored the .... So David won the prize.
4 If you want a better job, you will have to do .... work.
5 Make .... noise! You will disturb the neighbours.
6 There are too many people. We haven't got enough chairs. John said .... people would come.
7 Poor Jenny passed the .... exams in the class. She was last out of 30 students.
8 There's not enough water. We need .... rain.
9 John and Jenny haven't got much money. But Richard has the .... among all of us. He's very poor.
10 Rob has been round the world .... times than anyone else I know.

UNITS 25–26

A *Fill in the gaps the correct article.*

When (**1**) ...... people visit (**2**) ...... Eiffel Tower, they get (**3**) ...... magnificent view all over Paris. From (**4**) ...... top of (**5**) ...... tower, you can see many famous sights. You can also see how (**6**) ...... River Seine winds through Paris.

Paris is (**7**) ...... wonderful city. It is full of (**8**) ...... beautiful buildings. There are (**9**) ...... parks. And, of course, there are (**10**) ...... well-known restaurants. (**11**) ...... best restaurants are often those in (**12**) ...... small streets. But you have to know where to find them. I've never been to (**13**) ...... restaurant in Paris where (**14**) ...... food is poor.

B *Write the correct possessive form.*

15 That book belongs to me. It's ....
16 That's not your car. It belongs to David. It's ....
17 Are you sure that's ....? It doesn't look like the coat I bought.
18 That's .... boat. He bought it last year.
19 I like .... new furniture. Did it cost you a lot?
20 Mary says that picture is .... She bought it at a sale.

UNIT 27

Write this, that, these *or* those.

21 Put .... box here in the next room!
22 I don't like .... people who live in the house next to Mary.
23 I want .... picture you saw in the card shop.
24 I'll never forget .... film we saw last night.
25 I like .... flowers here, but .... over there are very dull.

UNITS 28–31

A *Complete the sentences with* some, any, no *or* none.

26 Have you got .... apples?
27 .... of the students were late. They all arrived on time.

28 I've got .... good news for you. You've passed the test.
29 There hasn't been .... rain for months.
30 .... of the books I borrowed were good. They were all badly written.
31 He's got .... money. He spent it all at the disco.
32 Have .... of your friends given money to the charity.

B *Complete these sentences with* many, much *or* a lot of.

33 How .... people have you invited to the party?
34 How .... money did you borrow?
35 There were .... interesting ideas in that book.
36 I can't find .... good books in the library.
37 .... the ideas you had have been used on this course.
38. Did you eat .... of the food at the holiday camp?
39. .... these answers are wrong.
40. I don't want to see .... of the students tomorrow.

C *Complete these sentences with* a few, few, a little *or* little.

41 Her father gave her .... money, so she had to work.
42 There were .... films that interested me, but not many.
43 It was disappointing. .... people came to greet him.
44 There was .... violence in the film, but not much.
45 .... of the people were very angry, but not many.
46 There was only .... of the food left after the children went into the kitchen.

D *Complete these sentences with* fewer, fewest, less, least, more *or* most.

47 John got .... marks than Mary in the test.
48 Robert buys .... of the newspapers every day. He likes reading all the news.
49 Alice eats .... than Irene, but she's still fat.
50 The Rolls-Royce engine makes the .... noise.

USE

FREQUENCY ADVERBS

1 When we want to talk about how often things happen, there are several adverbs we can use

> *always*
> *usually*
> *often*
> *sometimes*
> *seldom*
> *rarely*
> *never*

2 These adverbs usually go before the main verb.
*I **always meet** him on my way to school.*
*She **sometimes came** here on Mondays.*
*We will **never go** to that restaurant.*
*They have **often gone** to India for their holiday.*
*I don't **often see** him when I go to the cinema.*
*Did she **always come** here on Mondays?*
3 When the verb is *to be*, the adverbs come after the verb.
He's always very late.
She wasn't often angry.
Notes:
1 *Never* has a negative meaning, and we can say

either:
*We **will never go to** that restaurant.*
or
*We **won't ever go** to that restaurant.*
2 We don't use *sometimes* with the negative.
3 We can use *ever* for general questions:
Have you ever been to Italy?
4 These adverbs come after ordinary modals like *can,
must, shall, may*, etc.
*You **can sometimes** see the island from that hill.*
but before verbs like *have to* and *used to*:
*We **always have to** get there early.*
5 This diagram gives you an idea about the meaning
of these adverbs:

always 100%
usually 85%
often 70%
sometimes 50%
seldom 20%
rarely 20%
never ..0%

---

1   Write the correct order

Write the words in the sentences in the correct order.
Example:
met train often on they the
They often met on the train.

1 New has to been she Zealand never.
2 ridden ever you horse have a on?
3 usually I don't television watch.
4 never forget elephants.
5 postman twice always the rings.
6 cat does vegetables always your eat?
7 to in the they week restaurants go seldom.
8 Roger often town in we meet don't.
9 play park children the the often in.
10 usually do work train by come you to?
11 food she ever African eaten has?
12 seldom in Saturdays we on stay.
13 he family visits his never.
14 doesn't lunch usually she eat.
15 sea their holiday they take by often the.
16 fruit breakfast usually for eats she.
17 together cards play they often.
18 money you ever won have any?
19 at go we seldom away Christmas.
20 my met she has brother never.

2   Rewrite the sentences

Rewrite the sentences to include the adverb given.
Example:
They come here. (often)
They often come here.

1 He goes out on Sundays. (never)
2 Have you flown in a balloon? (ever)
3 Does he travel to the United States on Concorde? (always)
4 What do you do by the river in summer? (usually)
5 She's very clever. She passes all her exams. (always)
6 Rob reads before going to bed. (always)
7 I don't walk to work. (usually)
8 There isn't anyone ready to help you. (ever)
9 That wedding will take place. (never)
10 You can see fish jumping in this river. (sometimes)
11 Do you get up at 6 o'clock? (always)
12 We eat out. (often)
13 I like to go for a long walk. (sometimes)
14 She doesn't get home before 8 in the evening. (often)

15 We've been to China. (never)

16 Does she go to France on holiday? (always)

17 What does he do after work? (usually)

18 Anne likes to go sailing. (sometimes)

19 They drink coffee. (never)

20 When does she get to work? (usually)

3 Answer the questions

Answer the questions with Yes *or* No *and the adverb given.*

Example:

Do you sometimes have to stay late at work?

(no – never)

No, I never have to stay late at work.

1 Have you seen the Queen of England? (no – never)

2 Did you play in the park when you were a child? (yes – sometimes)

3 Do you go to the theatre? (yes – often)

4 Do you do exercise at home? (yes – always)

5 Will you remember me? (yes – always)

6 Have you ever been to Egypt? (yes – often)

7 Do you have to wash your own clothes? (no – never)

8 Do you walk to school? (yes – always)

9 Do you like space films? (yes – sometimes)

10 Can you introduce me to your boss. (no – never)

11 Have you visited her parents? (yes – often)

12 Did you ever see that play? (no – never)

13 Will you go there again? (no – never)

14 Do you eat fish? (yes – sometimes)

15 Did she learn to drive? (no – never)

16 Will you go back to Italy? (yes – often)

17 Has she seen your house? (no – never)

18 Does he play football on Saturday? (yes – always)

19 Did she drive very fast when she was young? (yes – always)

20 Do you have to stay late at work? (no – never)

4 Answer the questions

Answer the questions. Use the percentage shown at the end of the question to choose a frequency adverb.

Example:

How often do you go to the cinema in Italy? (20%)

Oh, I seldom went to the cinema in Italy.

1 How often does John play football on Saturdays? (85%)

2 How often does Jane cycle to work? (0%)

3 How often did you go to Josie's house for parties in London? (100%)

4 How often will Hannah see Roger in Paris? (50%)

5 How often can you miss school? (0%)

6 How often must I do my homework? (100%)

7 How often do you get up late in the morning? (100%)

8 How often do you buy new clothes? (20%)

9 How often has Sally been in hospital? (0%)

10 How often do you eat in restaurants? (85%)

11 How often have you moved house? (20%)

12 How often does she change her job? (70%)

13 How often do you leave work early? (20%)

14 How often did they go away at weekends? (100%)

15 How often have you borrowed money? (0%)

16 How often can you come to see me? (70%)

17 How often did she go swimming on holiday? (20%)

18 How often did you miss your class? (50%)

19 How often does the train get in late? (85%)

20 How often has he changed his car? (0%)

5 Complete the dialogue

Rob and Dave are talking about a friend. Complete the dialogue with an adverb suggested by the percentage shown.

Example:

Do you (100%) come here?

Do you always come here.

Rob: Does he (**1** 100%) .... go to see her on Saturday evening?

Dave: Oh, yes. He's (**2** 0%) .... missed a Saturday for three years.

Rob: And do they (**3** 100%) .... go to the cinema?

Dave: Oh no! They (**4** 50%) .... go to the disco. But he (**5** 0%) .... enjoys it.

Rob: I thought so. I've (**6** 20%) .... seen him at a disco.

Dave: They (**7** 85%) .... leave early when they go.

Rob: I've (**8** 70%) .... seen them in the park on Sunday.

Dave: Yes, they (**9** 85%) .... go there when it's not raining.

Rob: And he's (**10** 0%) .... had another girl-friend.

Dave: Oh yes. Before he met Jean, he (**11** 70%) .... went out with different girls, but that's finished now.

FORM AND USE

ADJECTIVES

Adjectives tell us more about nouns

the book – the blue book
the man – the old man

COMPARATIVE FORM

We use the comparative form when we are comparing two people or things:

Tom is tall (2 metres); Peter is tall (2.3 metres)
*Peter is **taller** than Tom.*
Gas is cheap (1.4p per unit); electricity is cheap (3.5p per unit)
*Gas is **cheaper** than electricity.*

Short adjectives (one or two syllables)

Add *-er* to the base

cheap – cheaper
soft – softer
loud – louder

but:

1 When an adjective ends in *y*, change the *y* to *i* and add *-er*

happy – happier
ugly – uglier

2 With some short adjectives, where there is a vowel before the final consonant, we double the last letter and then add *-er*

red – redder
hot -hotter
fat – fatter

Long adjectives (more than two syllables)

With long adjectives, we put *more* before the adjective

expensive – more expensive
dangerous – more dangerous

SUPERLATIVE FORM

We use the superlative form when we are comparing three or more people or things:

Peter is tall (2 metres); Tom is tall (2.3 metres); Richard is tall (2.5 metres)
*Peter is tall; Tom is taller than Peter; Richard is **the tallest**.*

Short adjectives

Add *-est* to the base. But:

1 When an adjective ends in *y*, change the *y* to *i* and add *-er*

happy – the happiest

2 With some short adjectives, where there is a vowel before the final consonant, we double the last letter, and then add *-er*

hot – the hottest

Long adjectives

Put *most* before the adjective

Note:

With the superlative form, we put *the* or another determiner, such as *my*, *his*, *her*

Who is the most beautiful girl in the world?
She is the richest of my aunts.
or
She is my richest aunt.

IRREGULAR ADJECTIVES

Ther are a few adjectives with irregular comparative and superlative forms:

good – better – best
bad – worse – worst
many – more – most
little – less – best

Note:

Far has two possible forms:
far – farther or *further – farthest* or *furthest*.

---

1   Fill in the gaps in the table

Positive	Comparative	Superlative
good	(1)	best
fair	fairer	(2) ....
(3)	more expensive	(4) ....
(5)	(6)	worst
ugly	(7)	ugliest
beautiful	(8)	(9) ....
little	(10)	least
(11)	younger	(12) ....
hot	(13)	(14) ....
(15)	bigger	(16) ....
important	(17)	(18) ....

2   Complete the sentences

What do you know about our galaxy? Complete the sentences by using the comparative or superlative form of the adjective in brackets.

1 Venus is the (hot) planet.
2 Jupiter is the (large) planet.
3 Saturn is (small) than Jupiter.
4 Uranus is many times (cold) than the coldest spot on earth.
5 Mars is (dry) than Earth.
6 Jupiter has (many) moons than the other planets.
7 The sun is (hot) than any of the planets.
8 Pluto is the (cold) of the planets.
9 Mercury is (near) to the sun than Venus.
10 Pluto is the (far) planet from the sun.

3 Complete the text

Below is a table of things to buy to help plants grow in your garden. Look at the information and then complete the text with the comparative or superlative form of the words in the box. Some of the words are used more than once. The first one has been done for you.

Product	Price	Size	Effectiveness
Growmore	£20.80	5 kilos	good
Fastgrow	£5.20	2 kilos	poor
Soilmix	£15.35	3 kilos	excellent
Fertile	£8.40	4 kilos	very good
Weedoff	£12.90	3 kilos	very poor
Plantup	£10.50	2 kilos	good

bad	cheap	expensive	good	large	small

We looked at six products for your garden. The *cheapest* of these per kilo was Fertile; the (**1**)......................... was Plantup. It cost £5.25 per kilo. Plantup was good, but not as good as Fertile which was (**2**)......................... for the grass. The (**3**)......................... one was Soilmix, but it also cost more than most of the others. However, you can buy Soilmix in (**4**)......................... amounts than Fertile. The (**5**)......................... product was Weedoff. It was also (**6**)......................... than many of the others. Growmore was good, but you have to buy (**7**)......................... amounts (at least 5 kilos) than you do for any of the others. For example, you can buy a (**8**)......................... amount of Soilmix. You can buy Fastgrow and Plantup in 2-kilo bags. Plantup is (**9**)......................... . We think the (**10**)......................... buy is Soilmix.

AS ... AS

1 When there are things which are the same, we put *as ... as* round the adjective
Mary is **as tall as** Ros.
2 We also use the negative form *not as ... as* to show things are not the same
Mr Brown **isn't as rich as** Mr Young. He is poorer.

4 Write sentences with *as ... as*

Example:
David / clever / Tom
David is as clever as Tom.

1 Martha / beautiful / Annie
2 His house / big / mine
3 January / long / March
4 April / short / June
5 Today / hot / yesterday
6 Fred / poor / Charlie
7 Jill / old / her husband
8 Cathy / tall / John
9 Derek / lively / his brother
10 Today, London / cold / Moscow
11 Alan / rich / Mary
12 You / young / Richard
13 John / scared / Peter
14 I / angry / you
15 This week / wet / last week
16 Philip / bad / his wife
17 Her hair / long / mine
18 Our dog / big / yours
19 Martin / handsome / Richard
20 I / hungry / Anne

5 Write sentences

Write sentences using not as ... as. *Then add another sentence using the comparative form of the opposite adjective.*

Example:
John / rich / Dave.
John isn't as rich as Dave. He is poorer.

1 Maisie / beautiful / Daisy
2 Pete / old / his wife
3 Pamela / generous / Paul
4 That house / big / yours
5 That film / sad / the one you saw last week
6 This winter / cold / last winter
7 That book / bad / the one you read last month
8 This exercise / difficult / exercise three
9 February / long / September
10 K2 / high / Everest
11 John / young / Peter
12 Paris / big / Tokyo
13 You / tall / Mary
14 This play / good / his first one
15 April / warm / August
16 Jane / tall / Catherine
17 March / dry / July
18 Potatoes / expensive / meat
19 The Channel / wide / Pacific
20 The film / good / his last one

Comparing Things 2: Adverbs

FORM AND USE

ADVERBS
Adverbs tell us more about verbs.
He runs. – He runs fast.
She works. – She works slowly.
Most adverbs are formed by adding *-ly* to the adjective
slow – slowly
But when an adjective ends in *-ly* we make an adverbial phrase
lively – in a lively way
Note:
There are some adverbs like *hard* and *fast* that are the same as the adjective forms.
*He is a **fast** runner.* (adjective)
*He runs **fast**.* (adverb)

COMPARATIVE AND SUPERLATIVE FORMS
The comparative and superlative are formed in the same way as for adjectives. Add-*er* and -*est* for short adverbs – don't forget to change the final *y* to *i*.
fast – faster – fastest
But generally we put *more* or *most* before adverbs.
slowly – more slowly – most slowly
Note:
There are two irregular forms.
well – better – best
badly – worse – worst

---

1 **Rewrite the sentences**

Rewrite the sentences using an adverb instead of the adjective.
Example:
Mary is a quicker worker than Martin.
Mary works more quickly than Martin.

1 Alan is a more careful driver than John.
2 Rita is a better singer than Harriet.
3 George is a more aggressive fighter than Frank.
4 This book gives a better report on China than yours.
5 Maisie is a livelier dancer than Anna.
6 That actress has a lovelier smile than her sister.
7 The cat's behaviour is more friendly than the dog's.
8 When he's at home, he speaks with a louder voice than when he's at work.
9 John is the worst swimmer of them all.
10 Fred is the best writer about paintings of this century.
11 Charles is a better tennis player than Peter.
12 Alice is a more beautiful singer than Elaine.
13 He is the fastest runner in the team.
14 She is a careless typist.
15 Frank is a harder worker than Tom.

2 **Fill in the gaps in the table**

Complete the gaps in this table

Positive	Comparative	Superlative
fast	(1)...................	fastest
well	(2)...................	(3)...................

(4)...................	more cheaply	(5)...................
(6)...................	(7)...................	worst
in a lively way	(8)...................	(9)...................
beautifully	(10)...................	(11)...................
hard	(12)...................	hardest
(13)...................	more cleverly	(14)...................
wisely	(15)...................	(16)...................
(17)...................	more slowly	(18)...................
(19)...................	(20)...................	most angrily
in an ugly way	(21)...................	(22)...................
(23)...................	more quickly	(24)...................
early	(25)...................	(26)...................
(27)...................	(28)...................	soonest
(29)...................	further	(30)...................

3 **Write the correct form**

Write the correct form of the adverb in brackets in each sentence.
Example:
That shop sells its apples *more cheaply* than the shop on the corner. (cheaply)

1 Jane drives .... than her husband. (fast)
2 He always behaves .... than any of the others in the class. (badly)
3 He plays football .... than anyone else in the team. (well)
4 John arrived at the party .... than Sally. (late)
5 But he left .... than she did. (early)
6 Those men have worked .... than anyone else here. (hard)

7 They play their music .... than anyone else in the house. (loudly)

8 She behaved the .... of all the people in the accident. (cheerfully)

9 Jane will get home the .... (soon)

10 He speaks .... than he used to now he is old. (quietly)

11 Mavis paints the .... in the class. (well)

12 He behaved the .... at the party. (badly)

13 Anne worked .... than Joan. (slowly)

14 He always slept .... in spring than he did in summer. (soundly)

15 She dressed .... than she could afford. (expensively)

AS ... AS
When things are the same, we put *as ... as* round the adverb
*Mary works **as hard as** Ros does.*
Note:
1 We often finish the comparison with part of the auxiliary verb *do* or with *can*
He worked as hard as he could. He couldn't have worked harder.
2 We also use the negative form *not as ... as* to show things are not the same
*Mr Brown **doesn't drive as fast as** Mr Smith. He drives more slowly.*

---

4 Write sentences with *as ... as*

Example:
John works / hard / Peter.
John works as hard as Peter.

1 David gets up / early / Mary
2 Jane stayed at the party / late / John
3 They sang / loudly / pop group
4 She greeted him / pleasantly / her sister did
5 He came / soon / he could
6 They ran / quickly / last year's winning team
7 They did / little / they could
8 We behaved / well / Tom's parents did
9 He will leave / soon / he can
10 They work / fast / they can
11 They sold the books / cheaply / they could
12 She cut the cloth / carefully / she could
13 David works / hard / Tom
14 May sings / beautifully / Kate
15 The parents behaved / stupidly / their children

5 Write sentences

Write sentences using not as ... as. *Then add another sentence using the opposite adverb with* very.
Example:
John drives / fast / Peter
John doesn't drive as fast as Peter. He drives very slowly.
She spoke / interesting / she could
She didn't speak as interestingly as she could. She spoke very boringly.

1 David gets up / early / Mary
2 Jane stayed at the party / late / John
3 They sang / loudly / pop group
4 She greeted him / pleasantly / her sister did
5 He came / early / he could
6 They ran / quickly / last year's winning team
7 They did / much / they could
8 We behaved / well / Tom's parents did
9 He will leave / late / he can
10 They work / fast / they can.

6 Write sentences.

Write sentences using not as .... as. *Then add another sentence using the opposite adverb in the comparative form.*
Example:
John drives / fast / Peter.
John doesn't drive as fast as Peter. He drives more slowly.
Dennis danced / in a dull way / Alan.
Dennis didn't dance in as dull a way as Alan. He danced in a more lively way.

1 She spoke / boringly / the main speaker.
2 Jane leave work / early / John
3 Dennis play football / in a dull way / Kevin.
4 They ran / quickly / last year's team.
5 They sang / loudly / the pop group.
6 Mary behave / kindly / Joan.
7 Frank behaved / happily / Helen.
8 He wrote / beautifully / Jane.
9 Dave spoke / well / Tom.
10 Henry left work / late / Alice.
11 Sally spoke / quietly / Nick.
12 Mike sold his car / cheaply / Rod sold his.
13 Tim play tennis / badly / Pete.
14 Jane's book sell / well / Mary's.
15 The Maths teacher spoke / fiercely / the History teacher.

UNIT 35 Prepositions of Place

at, in, on, by, near, above, under, to, towards, into, onto, out of, over

USE

POSITION
at
He stayed at the Royal Hotel.
Note:
We sometimes use *at* for villages and towns
She's staying overnight at Richmond.
in
She was standing in the shop.
Note:
We also use *in* for the weather.
She went for a walk in the rain.
The children were playing in the snow.
Notes:
We use *in* for countries and large towns or cities.
They live in Turkey.
They live in Istanbul.
on
They could see him on the roof.
Note:
Be careful about this difference.
The table is in the corner of the room.
They met on the corner of the street.
by/near
The woman stood by/near the car.
above
The book is on the shelf above the table.
under
The little boy hid under the table.

Note:
When talking about travelling, we say *by car/train/bus/bicycle/'plane/ship*, but *on foot*.
MOVEMENT
to
He's going to London tomorrow.
towards
She was walking slowly towards the man with a gun.
Notes:
Towards means going in the direction of. We don't know if the person reached the goal.
He's driving to London. = he intends to get there.
He's driving towards London. = he is going in the direction of London, but may not go there.
Note:
People often use *to* instead of *towards*.
Into
A man with a gun walked into the bank.
onto
He was climbing onto the roof.
Note:
You will sometimes see *on to* (two words). It is the same.
out of
People ran out of the bank.
over
The gunman jumped over the desk.

---

1 Fill in the gaps

Joan is moving into a new house and is telling the removal men where to put things. Fill in the gaps with the following prepositions of position: above by by by in in on on on on under

Put that table (**1**) .... the window. And those books (**2**) .... the table, put them (**3**) .... the shelves. The plates (**4**) .... the table go (**5**) .... that cupboard. (**6**) .... the door, there's a small chair. Put that (**7**) .... the corner over there. Where's the armchair? I saw it outside (**8**) .... the corner of the street a short time ago. You didn't leave it there, did you. Fetch it and put it (**9**) .... the fireplace. Then put that picture (**10**) .... the fireplace. There's a nail in the wall there. Don't drop those glasses (**11**) .... the floor. They'll break. Oh, how I hate moving house!

2 Complete the dialogue

John is telling Rosie about his plans to go to Berlin. Complete the paragraph with some prepositions of place.

I'm (**1**) .... Berlin in April. I want to be (**2**) .... Berlin for my birthday. I like sailing (**3**) .... the lakes and I like walking (**4**) .... the parks. In the evenings, I like to go (**5**) .... the bars. There are some wonderful people (**6**) .... some of them. Once I'm on the German motorway, I shall drive (**7**) .... Cologne. But before I get there, I shall take the road (**8**) .... Hanover. On the way, I shall stop (**9**) .... Liege (**10**) .... Belgium.

UNIT 36 Prepositions of Time
in, on, at

USE

in
1 With months and seasons
*They got married **in** June.*
*He had his holiday **in** the spring.*
2 For long festivals such as the Islamic festival of
Ramadan which lasts for a month
~~n~~ ~~~an~~ we cannot eat until sunset.

~~~~ and dates
~~~e~~ to work **on** Saturday.
*His birthday is **on** 20th September.*

at
1 For times on the clock
*The woman left **at** two o'clock.*
2 For short festivals such as the Christian festivals of
Christmas and Easter, which are only two or three
days.
*We always send each other cards **at** Christmas.*
Note:
We say *in the morning/the afternoon/the evening*, but *at
night*.

1 Complete the sentences

Complete these sentences with the correct prepositions.
Example:
I'm going to watch the football match *on* Saturday.

1 They'll come back ..... the evening.
2 They'll be on holiday ..... 1st June.
3 School starts ..... Tuesday.
4 I came to live here ..... 1995.
5 He often works ..... night.
6 They always have a family party ..... Christmas.
7 I'm meeting them ..... 5th May.
8 That house was built ..... 1897.
9 They have the Sidney–Hobart race ..... December.
10 ..... 2002, I'm going to finish work and travel round
the world.
11 I always like the weather ..... autumn.
12 It's her birthday .... March 19th.
13 I must go. I have to be there ..... 3 o'clock.
14 We'll see them again ..... Easter.
15 I'll be back ..... Wednesday.
16 He doesn't often go out ..... night.
17 She's gone abroad, but she'll be back ..... April.
18 The train leaves ..... 3.30.
19 Will you be here ..... the morning?
20 My holiday finishes ..... August 20th.

2 Complete the dialogue

*Alan and Bob are trying to arrange a meeting.
Complete the dialogue with prepositions of time. The
first one has been done for you.*

Alan: We must meet again. What about next
Tuesday?

Bob: That's no good. I go to the sports club *on*
Tuesday.
Alan: Wednesday then?
Bob: No. No. I'm usually free (**1**) ..... Wednesday,
but not next week. Friday?
Alan: No. I'm working (**2**) ..... the evening then.
Bob: Do you often work (**3**) ..... the evening?
Alan: No, but I am (**4**) ..... Friday.
Bob: We could meet late (**5**) ..... the evening. (**6**)
..... ten o'clock?
Alan: Oh, no. I don't like being out too late (**7**) .....
night. What about the following week?
Bob: But that's Christmas! We always go away
(**8**) ..... Christmas.
Alan: We could meet (**9**) ..... Saturday (**10**) ..... the
morning.
Bob: No. I'm playing football (**11**) ..... the
morning. The afternoon?
Alan: No, that's not possible. I always see my
mother (**12**) ..... the afternoon.
Bob: (**13**) ..... Saturday?
Alan: Yes. We'll have to wait until next year. What
are you doing (**14**) ..... January?
Bob: I'm going to India (**15**) ..... the 4th and I
come back (**16**) ..... the 29th. We could meet
(**17**) ..... February.
Alan: It's too cold (**18**) ..... February. March?
Bob: That's Easter. We always go away (**19**) .....
Easter.
Alan: I know. Let's meet (**20**) 2010
Bob: That's a long time ahead!

UNIT 37 *very /too / enough*

USE

1 Write *enough*

Add enough *to the words underlined in these sentences.*

1 He didn't run <u>fast</u>.
2 Have you got <u>money</u>?
3 She didn't work <u>hard</u>.
4 He's done <u>work</u>.
5 John wasn't <u>clever</u>.
6 The water wasn't <u>warm</u> to swim.
7 She wasn't <u>tall</u> to reach the top shelf in the cupboard.
8 The house wasn't <u>cheap</u> for him to buy.
9 There wasn't <u>rain</u> this winter.
10 The exercise wasn't <u>easy</u> for him.

2 Complete the sentences

Complete the sentences with too, very *or* enough.

1 The book was .... long, but I enjoyed it.
2 She didn't have .... money to buy the dress.
3 Unfortunately the red car was .... expensive, so he had to buy a smaller one.
4 Indonesia is a .... beautiful country. I love going there.
5 I didn't like that orange drink It was .... sweet.
6 At four, Jane is .... young to go to school, but she can start next year.
7 He ate .... much and felt ill all night.

8 You mustn't swim there. It's .... dangerous.
9 She got a .... large sum of money from her aunt and bought a Rolls-Royce.
10 He was driving the car .... fast through the town and was stopped by the police.

3 Complete the dialogue

Complete the dialogue with too, very *or* enough.

Dave: We must make this box tonight. Here are all the pieces.
Jill: I can't do it. It's (**1**) .... difficult.
Dave: You must try to do it. It's (**2**) .... important.
Jill: I don't care. I haven't got (**3**) .... time.
Dave: There's plenty of time. Now read the instructions (**4**) .... carefully.
Jill: I've done that. But that piece for the side of the box is (**5**) .... long and doesn't fit; and this piece for the top isn't long (**6**) ....
Dave: It's simple really. Now stop a moment and think hard.
Jill: I've thought hard (**7**) .... It's a (**8**) .... silly thing to do. I don't know why I'm helping you.
Dave: Because I'm paying you.
Jill: But it's not (**9**) .... money. It's (**10**) .... little for all this work.

UNIT 32

A *Write words in these sentences in the correct order.*

1 bus by work John always to goes
2 friends doesn't her see often Sally
3 in restaurant she's that sometimes
4 tennis often Mary play with you do?
5 at we theatre seen seldom play have bad that a
6 key loses often he his
7 late always be we mustn't
8 holidays spend they in their usually Britain
9 trains early are the always
10 come he home always does early

B *Write the correct adverb according to the percentage given.*

11 Do you (100%) go to Greece for your holidays?
12 No, I (50%) go to the Seychelles.
13 It (20%) rains there.
14 No, but you (70%) get cloudy days.
15 I've (0%) heard that before.

UNIT 33

Write the correct form of the adjective.

16 She is the (beautiful) person in the room.
17 I did (good) than my friend in the exam.
18 My house is old, but Mr Brown's house is (old).
19 The disaster is (bad) than I thought.
20 I haven't seen a play as (bad) as that one.
21 That's the (good) team in the league.
22 This is the (wet) summer for 200 years.
23 John is (tall) than Richard.
24 Keith is the (clever) person in this class.
25 I haven't seen a (big) tree in this park.

UNIT 34

Write the correct form of the adverb.

26 Sally can't run as (fast) as Daisy.
27 Come as (early) as you can.
28 Tom danced in a (lively) manner than his girl-friend.
29 They've worked the (hard) in the class.
30 He behaved (badly) than his brother.
31 Can you walk a little (fast). It's getting late?
32 Do you feel (well) than you did yesterday?
33 I can't believe he worked as (hard) as that.
34 He spoke (angrily) than was necessary.
35 He played (happily) at his friends' than at home.

UNITS 35–36

A *Complete the description of this picture with the correct preposition.*

There is a table (**36**) .... the garden, and (**37**) .... the table, there are some flowers. (**38**) .... the table there is a large box. (**39**) .... the box, there is a cat. A man is coming (**40**) .... the house with a small child. They are walking (**41**) .... table.

B *Write the correct preposition in these sentences.*

42 I'll come .... Wednesday.
43 John will be here .... five o'clock.
44 The exams are .... June.
45 What are you doing .... Christmas.

UNIT 37

Write too, very or enough.

46 There are .... many people in this room. It's crowded.
47 They haven't sold .... tickets for the concert. They'll lose money.
48 That house is .... old. It's the oldest in the town.
49 David is .... young to see that film.
50 Peter isn't old .... to get married yet.

FORM AND USE

RELATIVE CLAUSES

Look at this dialogue.

David: *John has met the woman.*
John: *Which woman?*
David: *The woman **who lives next door to me**.*

In David's answer, *who lives next door* is a relative clause. A relative clause tells you more about a person, animal or thing. It answers the question *Which?* In the example above, John has asked, '*Which woman*'?

WHO/THAT

The relative clause for people begins with *who* or *that*.

David: *The footballer scored four goals in the match.*
John: *Which footballer?*
David: *The footballer **who signed for the club last week**.*

WHICH/THAT

When we are talking about animals or things, the relative clause begins with *which* or *that*.

Mary: *David's taken the book.*
Susan: *Which book?*
Mary: *The book **which was lying on the table**.*

Mandy: *The cat ate my pet fish.*
Vera: *Which cat?*
Mandy: *The cat **that lives across the road**.*
Remember!
People: *who* or *that*
Animals/things: *which* or *that*
Note:
Who, *that* and *which* are relative pronouns.

---

1   Complete the sentences

Complete the sentences with that.
Example:
The boy *that* sits in the front row by the window is now the captain of his class.
I want to see the film *that* is coming to the cinema next week.

1 The man .... is married to Nicole has been an actor for twenty years.
2 I liked the dress .... was on display in the shop window.
3 Give me the plates .... are on the shelf over there.
4 She knows all about the accident .... happened last week.
5 I haven't seen anybody .... looks like Antonio in here.
6 The only disco .... played good music in this town has closed.
7 I want the three dolls .... cost £20 each.
8 The school .... opened last month has a very well-known head teacher.
9 The housewife .... is a mathematician has already been on three TV quiz shows.
10 I want to know the name of the person .... told you about me.

2   Replace *that*

Now do Exercise 1 again and replace that *with* who *or* which.
Example:
The boy *who* sits in the front row by the window is now the captain of his class.
I want to see the film *which* is coming to the cinema next week.

1 The man .... is married to Nicole has been an actor for twenty years.
2 I liked the dress .... was on display in the shop window.
3 Give me the plates .... are on the shelf over there.
4 She knows all about the accident .... happened last week.
5 I haven't seen anybody .... looks like Antonio in here.
6 The only disco .... played good music in this town has closed.
7 I want the three dolls .... cost £20 each.
8 The school .... opened last month has a very well-known head teacher.
9 The housewife .... is a mathematician has already been on three TV quiz shows.
10 I want to know the name of the person .... told you about me.

3 Join the sentences

Join the sentences with who *or* which *to make one sentence.*

Examples:

Who was the man? He fell down near the station.

Who was the man who fell down near the station?

1 Where is the book? It was here on the table.
2 David sold me the horse. It won the big race last week.
3 Mary has bought a house. It used to be a shop.
4 That's the boy. He took Jane's bicycle.
5 The girl has gone to university. She came top in the physics exam.
6 The dog is very dangerous. It lives near the village shop.
7 John wrote the letter. It came this morning.
8 Give it to the little girl. She found our cat.
9 He doesn't like that film. It was at the cinema last week.
10 That's the woman. She came to live here last month.

4 Complete the dialogue

Complete the dialogue with who *or* which.

Tim: Do you know the girl?
Jim: Which girl?
Tim: The girl (**1**) .... lives next door to you.
Jim: Of course. And she has a great car (**2**) .... does 200 kilometres an hour.
Tim: She doesn't drive it at 200 kph, does she?
Jim: Oh yes, she does. In Germany, she drives on the road (**3**) .... goes from Berlin to Hamburg.
Tim: But that's dangerous!
Jim: No! Everyone (**4**) .... travels on that road goes very fast.
Tim: It is dangerous. People (**5**) .... drive very fast are dangerous.
Jim: But these are roads (**6**) .... are made for fast drivers.
Tim: No. They are roads for people (**7**) .... don't want to go through town centres.
Jim: It's the same thing. I have a friend (**8**) .... drives slowly. He doesn't go on these fast roads.
Tim: Fast cars are dangerous.

Jim: No. People are dangerous. And people (**9**) .... are dangerous mustn't drive cars (**10**) .... go fast.

5 Add the clauses

Add these clauses to the story below. Write who *or* which *in front of them. The first one has been done for you.*

which played at the Apollo last night
.... has won his heart
.... was near his home
.... went to school with him
.... lived in a small house
.... have played with him for five years
.... was wearing a green dress
.... was for all people in their year in the district
.... have never seen the girl before
.... was a heart surgeon
.... was usually the school gym

Jim Grindey, the singer in the rock group *which played at the Apollo last night*, is going to marry a girl (**1**) .... This has surprised the other players (**2**) .... but (**3**) .... Jim won't tell anyone the name of the girl (**4**) .... , but says that he has always loved her.

They met at the school (**5**) .... He came from a poor family (**6**) .... The girl is the daughter of a doctor (**7**) .... He was afraid to speak to her at first. Then, when they were fourteen, they both went to a party (**8**) .... It wasn't a good party. The boys stood on one side of the hall (**9**) .... and the girls on the other. There was a girl (**10**) .... – Jim's favourite colour. She was the doctor's daughter and she came and spoke to him. From that moment they were in love.

What about the last five years as a rock singer?

'I always thought of her – the girl in the green dress!' Jim says.

UNIT 39 Relative Clauses 2: Object
whom (who), which, that, no relative

FORM AND USE

WHOM (WHO) / NO RELATIVE
Look at this dialogue
David: *Did you see the man?*
John: *Which man?*
David: ***Richard met the man last week.***

We can put this in one sentence
David: *Did you see the man **whom** Richard met last week?*
Whom replaces *the man* as the object of *met*.
But:
In conversation we don't usually use *whom*. We can replace *whom* with *who*
*Did you see the man **who** Richard met last week?*
or with no relative
Did you see the man Richard met last week?

WHICH / NO RELATIVE
Mary: *David's taken the book.*
Susan: *Which book?*
Mary: *The book **which I bought for you**.*
With things we use *which* or no relative.
Mary: David's taken the book **which** I bought for you
or
Mary: David's taken the book I bought for you.
Remember!
People – *whom/who* or no relative, or *that*
Animals/things – *which* or no relative, or *that*

---

1 Complete the sentences

Complete the sentences with who / whom or which.
Example:
I didn't like the book *which* you gave me.

1 He gave the flowers to the first girl .... he saw in a red dress.
2 She liked the horse .... she rode in the park last Sunday.
3 I don't like writing all the exercises .... the teacher wants.
4 They rewarded the man .... the girl praised.
5 Nobody liked the man .... Tim introduced.
6 Put the picture .... I bought last week on the wall in the lounge.
7 I loved the trees .... they cut down last week.
8 John dislikes that woman .... is very clever.
9 Give him back the money .... you took for the meal.
10 I don't know the road .... he suggested was quick.

2 Join the sentences

Join the sentences to make one sentence with no relative.
Example:
Give me the money! You borrowed it last week.
Give me the money you borrowed last week.

1 I want to see the film. Jane saw it yesterday.

2 Where is the house? John and Mary have just bought it.
3 They don't like that girl. Jimmy took her to the cinema.
4 Do you know the man? Your dog bit him.
5 I haven't read the book. You bought it for my birthday.
6 That's the tall woman. Pamela saw her in the park.
7 John's got a computer. Paul wants it.
8 Now Joanne's climbed the hills. Dick climbed them on his last holiday.
9 Let's play that game. We played it last night.
10 The animals ate the food. We gave it to them.

3 Join the sentences

Now do Exercise 2 again and join the sentences with who or which.
Example:
Give me the money! You borrowed it last week.
Give me the money which you borrowed last week.

1 I want to see the film. Jane saw it yesterday.
2 Where is the house? John and Mary have just bought it.
3 They don't like that girl. Jimmy took her to the cinema.
4 Do you know the man? Your dog bit him.
5 I haven't read the book. You bought it for my birthday.
6 That's the tall woman. Pamela saw her in the park.
7 John's got a computer. Paul wants it.

8 Now Joanne's climbed the hills. Dick climbed them on his last holiday.

9 Let's play that game. We played it last night.

10 The animals ate the food. We gave it to them.

4 Write the correct relative pronoun

Write the correct relative pronoun who *or* which.

Mavis: Did you like the music (**1**) .... John was playing?

David: I never like the music (**2**) .... John plays.

Mavis: But he has a good group. They're all musicians (**3**) .... I like.

David: I don't like the drummer (**4**) .... they found in Italy.

Mavis: Why not? I didn't like the one (**5**) .... they had before.

David: He played well. I don't usually like music (**6**) .... they do for drums, but I liked him.

Mavis: I like all music. I like the music (**7**) .... they write for piano, guitar, anything.

David: Do you like the music (**8**) .... the great composers wrote?

Mavis: Who are the composers (**9**) .... you think are great?

David: Those (**10**) .... people like, such as Mozart, Bach and Beethoven.

Mavis: Oh, I don't like those. I like pop composers.

5 Add the clauses

Add these subject and object clauses to the story below. Write who *or* which *in front of them. The first one has been done for you.*

who people admired but did not like
.... the townspeople were afraid of
.... he talked to or played with
.... he owned
.... he bought
.... people in the town admired
.... he built himself
.... he was at school with
.... his aunt owned
.... he went to
.... he took from his workers

Richard Mabey, *who people admired but did not like,* died last week. He lived in a large house (**1**) .... from money (**2**) .... He was the ninth child in a rough family (**3**) .... At the school (**4**) ...., he sat alone at the back of the class. He had no friends (**5**) .... When he left school, he worked in a shop (**6**) .... He quickly learned the business and soon his aunt, (**7**) .... gave him the shop. He worked hard and soon there was another shop (**8**) .... After a few years, there were many shops in the town (**9**) .... He gave work to many people (**10**) .... They didn't like him and he didn't pay well. But there was no other work.

6 Make sentences

Arrange the words in the right order, then write who *or* which *in at the right place in the sentences.*

Example:
fast car very he new goes the bought
The new car he bought goes very fast
The new car which he bought goes very fast.
like the they holiday didn't they met people on
They didn't like the people they met on holiday.
They didn't like the people who they met on holiday.

1 chair bought last the that's I week
2 you the is pianist town heard radio on our next last week the night visiting
3 house lives like I he don't in the
4 good sold no he car the is us
5 everybody David liked a wrote play
6 play old-fashioned music is you the very
7 sold jewellery Mary husband gave the her her
8 very clothes he are old wears the
9 didn't police the the to speak they man wanted
10 married he woman the rich very is
11 boss worker that's last promoted the week the
12 down trees they dangerous the cut were very
13 always woman you opposite I speak to live the
14 nobody film that's a likes
15 wanted man father her she marry like the didn't to
16 John give you sent me letter the
17 eat John in always I restaurants recommends
18 cousin the party you girl brought going to to marry my the is
19 music Tuscany liked he the heard he in
20 wild garden you in saw I catch cat the must my

USE

WHOSE
1 Look at these sentences:
The **woman** has gone to live in France. **Her** father died last year.
We can join them together with *whose*.
That woman **whose** father died last year has gone to live in France.
2 We can also use *whose* for things.
She reads Cosmopolitan – a **magazine** for women. **Its** readership fell last year.
This can become
She reads Cosmopolitan – a magazine for women **whose** readership fell last year.
OF WHOM
When the relative pronoun *who* follows a 'quantity' word, such as *some, any, many, few*, etc. we use *of whom*.
The executives are given cars by the company.
Many of the executives live in villages a long way from the offices.

The executives, **many of whom** live in villages a long way from their offices, are given cars by the company.
Note:
We also use *whose* or *of whom* for animals, especially household pets.
OF WHICH
For things we usually use *of which*.
He joined the **golf club**. The majority of **its** members were over sixty.
This becomes
He joined the golf club **of which** the majority of members were over sixty.
It is more usual, however, to put *of which* after the noun it is qualifying.
He joined the **golf club** the majority of members **of which** were over sixty.
Note:
After a preposition, we never use *that* as a relative pronoun.

---

1 **Describe the people**

Describe the people, animals or objects.
Example:
boy / ears / large
The boy whose ears are large.
book / three films / made
The book of which three films have been made.

1 horse / owner / very rich
2 girl / hair / long and blonde
3 car / people / spoke highly
4 actor / wife / left him
5 writer / talent / very great
6 jewel / owner / sold for £120,000
7 town / bus service / perfect
8 house / owner / bought for £1 million
9 painting / many copies / made
10 club / most members / very young
11 woman / husband / football star
12 tree / red leaves / are admired by everyone
13 John / photographs / people liked a lot
14 dog / owner / blind
15 schools / pupils / very bad

2 **Complete the sentences**

Complete the sentences with whose, of whom *or* of which.
Example:
I know the man *whose* house is by the canal.

1 That's the woman .... husband works for the United Nations.
2 They've bought the house, the previous owners .... went to America.
3 A book .... nobody had heard won the first prize.
4 He worked for that agency the owners .... were very famous.
5 The workers, the majority .... came from the north of the country, were pleased the company was opening a branch in the north.
6 Those birds, many .... come from South Africa, will leave here in autumn.
7 He likes to help people .... families are in difficulty.
8 That's the boy .... dog destroyed my garden.
9 I'm going to see the play the writer .... used to live next door to me.
10 I want to see the exhibition of those old paintings, many .... were only found last year.

11 These are the jewels, many .... are worth thousands of dollars.

12 Near that rubbish pile I found some books, many .... are very valuable.

13 I met Mr Brown .... father died last week.

3 Join the sentences

Join these sentences, using whose *or of whom.*

1 The students work on the boats in their holidays. Many of them have rich parents.

2 The captains are all good teachers. Their boats are designed for training work.

3 The drivers arrived at the racing track early. Most of the drivers were from Brazil.

4 The champion jockey lost the big race. His horse was very old.

5 The policeman arrested the thieves. Some of them were well-known criminals.

6 The bank manager spoke to the students. A few of them had no money in the bank.

7 The doctor spoke kindly to the old man. The old man's wife was very ill.

8 The woman was very proud. Her son came top in the exam.

9 That's the dog. Its owner doesn't feed it properly.

10 Is that the man? His daughter married a famous singer last week.

11 The girl was very angry. Her new dress was torn at the cleaners.

12 The teacher told the children to stay inside. Many of them had no heavy coats for the cold weather.

13 The writer didn't like being famous. His novel won the most important prize.

4 Join these sentences

Join the sentences, using whose, of whom *or* of which.
Example:
That's the man. His father owns the supermarket.
That's the man whose father owns the supermarket.

1 MaryLou lives in Bombay now. Her mother was a famous artist.

2 Give the money to the first person. His car was registered in 1996.

3 The football club is near the electricity station. Terry is a member of it.

4 Shakespeare's plays are still performed after three hundred years. Several of them are comedies.

5 There are six Indian restaurants in this town. Five of

them are owned by the same man.

6 I don't want to read that book. People speak very badly of it.

7 Daisy liked the animals. Their owners looked after them well.

8 They bought the diamond. Its original owner was the world's richest woman.

9 Those are the reporters. Some of them angered the President.

10 Don't go with that group of travellers. Most of them have never travelled before.

11 Let's go to meet the artist. His paintings have won many prizes.

12 I want to see the play. The critics spoke very highly of it.

13 Those are our holiday photographs. Half of them were taken by my brother.

5 Add the clauses

Add these clauses to the story below. Write whose *or* of which *in front of them. The first one has been done for you.*

.... the owner lived in Australia
.... the workers were unhappy
.... the roof was badly damaged
.... many were very old and valuable
whose life was always difficult
.... car John crashed
.... father knew the man
.... some his father had given him
.... the managers were always sacking people
.... father was very rich
.... none are known

John, *whose life was always difficult*, had problems. He was living in a house (**1**).............. and (**2**).............. , so the rain came in. He had no money to repair it. His girl-friend (**3**).............. wanted him to stay at her house, but her father didn't like him. John wanted to be a songwriter. He wrote many songs, (**4**).............. . So he had no money and worked for a company (**5**).............., and (**6**).............. if they didn't work ten hours every day. Yesterday, John got some money by selling records (**7**).............., and (**8**).............. . But he still owed some money to a man (**9**).............. . What could he do? His friend Tom, (**10**).............., told him to run away.

Relative Clauses 4: Place and Time
on which; in which; when; where

USE

IN WHICH / WHERE
Look at these sentences about places.
*Number 170 is **the house**. I was born **there**.*
We can join them together with *in which*
*Number 170 is the house **in which** I was born.*
But we usually say
*No 170 is the house **where** I was born.*
Note:
When it is a specific place, we only use *where*.
I saw it in London, where I stayed with my friends.
She bought it in Korea, where she went for a holiday.
ON WHICH / WHEN / IN WHICH
1 Look at these sentences about time.
*That was **the day**. My father died **on that day**.*
We can join them together with *on which*
*That was the day **on which** my father died.*
But we usually say

*That was the day **when** my father died.*
2 For *day* or *night*, we use *on*
*The day **on which** my father died.*
for *week* or *month* or *year*, we use *in*
*The year **in which** he went to university.*
Notes:
1 It is common with time relatives to use either *that* or
no relative.
That was the day that my father died.
or
That was the day my father died.
2 When it is a specific date or year, we only use *when*,
never *in which* or *on which*.
*I saw it on 29th March, **when** I was in London.*
*They worked for Shell in 1997, **when** they left
university.*

1 Join the sentences

Join the sentences with in which *or* on which.
Example:
John has been to the museum. There is an old map of
the town there.
*John has been to the museum in which there is an old
map of the town.*

1 He arrived there on the day. There was a circus in
the town that day.
2 She remembered the days. She had been happy on
those days.
3 They bought the house. The old man died in it.
4 I've been back to the church. I got married in it.
5 He's left the town. He was born in it.
6 That was the year. My son was born.
7 I remember the day. I bought my first computer.
8 She's forgotten the village. She grew up in it.
9 Enjoy the time. You are young and strong.
10 You mustn't go into the rooms. They keep their
private possessions in them.
11 I've read the book. The author criticizes the
government in it.
12 She's seen the play six times. They sing her
favourite song in it.
13 September is the month. I go on holiday in that
month every year.
14 That's the field. The children play football in it.
15 I'd like to go back to the time. I lived in Japan in
that time.

2 Join the sentences

Join the sentences with when *or* where.
Example:
Nicki went to Kuala Lumpur. The world's tallest
building is there.
*Nicki went to Kuala Lumpur, where there is the world's
tallest building.*

1 That's the house. The murder happened there.
2 That was the year. I met my wife then.
3 Mary met David in 1996. She was in Cairo then.
4 He became President in that year. We won the
World Cup that year.
5 Peter's working in that building. They have a lot of
exhibitions there.
6 I want to live on a tropical island. There's lots of
sun and fruit there.
7 Maisie has lived in Turkey since 1993. She teaches
English there.
8 You must plant those flowers in the spring. The
ground is just right then.
9 Get off the train at that station. You can see the new
football stadium there.
10 There's not much happening in the town. I used to
live there.
11 This is the desert. They broke the world land-speed
record here.
12 Jenny has the photograph. You're dressed as a
clown in it.

13 In the park there's an old hut. We used to hide there when we were children.

14 I remember the day. The President was shot on that day.

15 Jean passed her exams in the year. Most students failed in that year.

3 Replace the words

Replace the underlined words with where *or* when.
Example:
How deep was the lake <u>in which</u> you saw the monster?
*How deep was the lake **where** you saw the monster?*

1 Steve wanted to return to the town <u>in which</u> he was born.

2 Josie liked the sunflowers in the garden <u>in which</u> they performed the play.

3 Alan remembered the day <u>on which</u> he became head of the Institute.

4 There will be a time <u>in which</u> there is peace in the world.

5 Come to the islands <u>on which</u> the sun always shines.

6 Rob put the card from Jane in the box <u>in which</u> he kept special things.

7 Come any Wednesday except on the one <u>on which</u> I have to go to Manchester.

8 The thieves broke into the house <u>in which</u> the old man lived.

9 On days <u>on which</u> there is no fog or rain, you can see the hills ten kilometres away.

10 How high was the mountain <u>on which</u> you saw the footprint of the Yeti?

11 Did you see the house <u>in which</u> the murder happened.

12 Mary went to Paris on the day <u>on which</u> there was a fire in the Channel Tunnel.

13 They plan to get married in the week <u>in which</u> they graduate.

14 That's the park <u>in which</u> I used to play as a child.

15 He didn't want to go near the lake <u>in which</u> the accident happened.

4 Replace *when* or *where*

Replace when *or* where *with* in which *or* on which.
Example:
I can't remember a time when so much had to be done.
I can't remember a time in which so much had to be done.

1 Jeffrey bought the house where he now lives in 1987.

2 The day when I met you was the luckiest day in my life.

3 That was the year when we won the tennis championship.

4 December was the month when she left home.

5 That's the bank where they've stored those famous paintings.

6 Do you know the year when the first climbers reached the top of Everest?

7 Put the books in that room where you see the new desk.

8 I like restaurants where they don't play music.

9 Have you seen the castle where the last emperor lived?

10 I remember the day when the war started.

11 He last saw her on the day when we had the very bad storm.

12 Jane lives near the park where I used to play football.

13 Easter was the time when he always visited his aunt.

14 Paul showed his mother the house where he lived with the other students.

15 That's the club where they have the famous painting of the town.

5 Complete the story

Complete the story with when *or* where. *The first one has been done for you.*

There are some places *where* there are always a lot of tourists. The Lake District in northern England is one of them. On a summer's day (**1**) .... the weather is very hot and sunny, there are thousands of people. Those small towns (**2**) .... famous writers lived attract a lot of people. So do the lakes (**3**) .... you can get a boat across. And the hills (**4**) .... the climbers go are also crowded.

   The summer (**5**) .... I took my last school exam was hot and sunny. At the end of term, I walked away from the school (**6**) .... I had studied for nine years, and went to the station, (**7**) .... I met three of my friends and we caught a train to the Lakes. That was the first time (**8**) .... I got a train (**9**) .... you could sleep. I didn't sleep. I was too excited. I wasn't at school, (**10**) .... I had to work. I wasn't in the house (**11**) .... I lived with my parents. I was free. This was the time (**12**) .... I started to live my own life.

UNIT 42   Conjunctions 1: *when / while*

USE

WHILE

1 When one event takes place during the continuation of another.
Joan visited her brother while she was travelling round the world.
The visit happened during the world trip and the focus is on the visit to her brother. You put *while* at the beginning of the part of the sentence which shows the longer event.

2 For two events happening at the same time.
Robin was listening to the radio while he was driving along the motorway.
Here, *while* can go at the beginning of either part of the sentence, but usually you put it at the beginning of the main event.

3 *While* is usually followed by a verb in a continuous form.
While I was crossing the road, . . .
While she is visiting her friend, . . .

4 When we use *while*, the event is still continuing.
While he was driving along the motorway . . .
(This is an unfinished event in the past.)
Note:
Put a comma between the two clauses only when the *while*-clause is first.

WHEN

1 We use *when* to show one event has interrupted another.

Robin was driving along the motorway, when the accident occurred.

2 *When* can only be used at the beginning of the part of the sentence which shows the interruption.

driving along the motorway | accident occurred

3 When we use *when*, the verb is usually in a simple tense.
When the accident occurred . . .
When I go to France . . .
Note:
Put a comma between the two clauses only when the *when* clause is first.

TENSES WITH WHEN / WHILE

1 You can use an imperative clause after a *when*-or *while*-clause.
*While you are preparing the meal, **watch** the TV news.*
*When you see John, **tell** him to come early.*

2 When these conjunctions are used for future events, the verb after *when / while* is usually in the present tense.
*David will meet Mary **when** he **finishes** his work.*
*David will have lunch **while** he **is finishing** his work.*

3 You can also use the present perfect with *when*.
*David will meet Mary **when** he **has finished** his work.*

---

1 Match the parts

Match the parts of these sentences. The first one has been done for you.

1 While they were playing tennis,
2 While I was walking in the park,
3 When she goes home at night,
4 While she is watching television,
5 When John saw the wild dog,
6 While you are staying in Krakow,
7 When you arrive at the station,
8 While you are waiting for the taxi,
9 When he heard the news,
10 While you are in London,
11 When I saw you,

a) stay at the entrance.
b) go and visit the British Museum.
c) you will be able to see the trumpeters.
d) I saw a wild dog.
e) telephone for a taxi.
f) he wanted to tell his wife.
g) it started to rain.
h) I was having lunch.
i) her husband cooks the dinner.
j) she always watches television.
k) he hid behind a tree.

....

2 Write the correct tense

Example:
When they (get) the contract, they'll start the work.
When they get the contract, they'll start the work.

1 When you (finish), you can go home.
2 When John (see) Mary, she was crying.
3 Mary (be) very upset when she saw the dead cat.
4 There (be) nobody important here when Terry and Nelson leave.

5 When Anne (arrive), the children will be happy.
6 The children (be) happy when Anne arrived.
7 The thieves came when the house (be) empty.
8 When I (be) on holiday, I'll stay at the best hotel.
9 I'll visit your country when you (have) a new government.
10 The visitors (have to) leave when the Queen comes.

3 Write the correct tense

Example:
While you (sleep) tonight, I'll be working.
While you're sleeping tonight, I'll be working.

1 While John (sit) outside the café, a car crashed into the shop next door.
2 They (hear) a strange sound while they were getting ready for the concert.
3 While they were going to the concert, they (listen) to the music on the radio.
4 Jane's husband looks after the children while she (work) at the office.
5 We'll go to the park while Helen and Tony (play) tennis.
6 The actor was acting in the theatre at night while he (make) a film during the day.
7 While John (study) at university, he will have to work as a guide to the city.
8 David shared a flat with some students while he (live) in Rome.

4 Answer the questions

These are notes of what happened at Mary's and Peter's house one evening between 5.00 and 8.00.
Read the notes, then answer the questions.

5.00–5.30	Mary and Peter playing tennis	5.15	John arrive
5.30–6.00	having tea	5.45	phone rang / wrong number
6.00–6.15	Mary working in study	6.05	loud explosion
		6.10	Peter phone police
6.15–6.30	saving things in house	6.20	police arrive
		6.25	firemen arrive
6.30–6.45	Mary and Peter talking to the police	6.35	John's wife arrive
6.30–6.45	John checking damage		
6.45–7.00	police listening to John's report	6.50	firemen left
7.00–8.00	clearing damaged room	7.05	police left
		7.30	floor collapsed

Examples:
When did John arrive?
While Mary and Peter were playing tennis.

1 When did the phone ring with a wrong number?
2 What was the first thing that happened while Mary was working in her study?
3 What was Mary doing when Peter phoned the police?
4 When did the firemen arrive?
5 What was John doing while Mary and Peter were talking to the police?
6 What were Mary and Peter doing when John's wife arrived?
7 What was happening when the firemen left?
8 When did the police leave?
9 What were they doing when the floor collapsed?
10 What was Mary doing when there was a loud explosion?

5 Write the questions

Using the notes in Exercise 4, write the questions for these answers.
Examples:
The police left.
What was the first thing that happened while they were clearing the room?

1 John arrived.
2 While they were having tea.
3 There was a loud explosion.
4 While Mary was working in her study.
5 While they were saving things in the house.
6 The firemen arrived.
7 She arrived while they were talking to the police.
8 He was checking the damage.
9 While the police were listening to John's report.
10 The floor collapsed.

USE

BEFORE
Look at these sentences.
Joan visited her brother before she went on a world trip.
Before she went on a world trip, Joan visited her brother.
First event: visit her brother
Second event: world trip
Here the first event is more important.
Note:
Put a comma between the two clauses when the *before*-clause is first.

AFTER
Look at these sentences.
After she visited her brother, she went on a world trip.
She went on a world trip after she visited her brother.
First event: visit her brother

Second event: world trip
Here the second event is more important.
Note:
Put a comma between the two clauses when the *after* clause is first.
Notes:
1 When *before* is used for future events, the verb is usually in the present tense in the part of the sentence after the conjunction.
*Before David **meets** Mary, he will finish his work.*
2 When *after* is used for future events, we usually use the present perfect in the part of the sentence after the conjunction.
*David will meet Mary **after** he **has finished** his work.*

---

1 **Write the correct tense**

Example:
I'll see you after I (finish) my work.
I'll see you after I finish / have finished my work.

1 I saw him after he (speak) to the head teacher.
2 They (quarrel) after they went in Rome.
3 She (see) him every week, after she goes swimming.
4 The fire started after he (leave) home in the morning.
5 They'll play tennis after they (have) dinner.
6 We ('phone) you after we arrive at the hotel.
7 He won't see her again after he (leave) this job.
8 I can't meet you after I (leave) work. It'll be too late.
9 She'll only see the film after she (read) the book.
10 She'll spend a few days in India after she (be) to Australia.
11 He (watch) television after he has had his dinner.
12 He (go) to the concert after he read the reviews.
13 We'll enjoy seeing your photographs after you (come) home from holiday.
14 Jane got Peter's letter after she (meet) him in the town.
15 Charles (help) you after he has come back from the shops.

2 **Write the correct tense**

Example:
I (see) you before I go on holiday next week.
I'll see you before I go on holiday next week.

1 He was very lonely, before he (meet) her.
2 You'll see a bookshop on your right before you (reach) the street where I live.
3 Every Friday, he goes to the bank before he (go) the office.
4 Hurry up! The taxi (be) here before you're ready.
5 He used to do some exercise before he (go) to work.
6 David (like) swimming before he had the accident.
7 Sarah was a teacher before she (become) a singer.
8 The house (be) destroyed before the firemen arrived.
9 I won't finish the work before you (arrive) on Saturday.
10 John (get) his exam results before he goes on holiday.
11 They built those houses over there before they (get) permission.
12 You'll be in Rome before David (arrive) in Athens.
13 The film (begin) before we get to the cinema.
14 They won't give you the tickets before the train (leave).
15 She (not know) the result of the game before she heard it on the radio.

3 Join the sentences

Join the sentences using before.
Example:
I'll meet you outside the bookshop. Then we'll go to the cinema.
I'll meet you outside the bookshop before we go to the cinema.

1 He used to see her in the park. Then he spoke to her.
2 David'll go to work. Then he'll go to the football match.
3 Every day, Sally has breakfast. Then she listens to the radio.
4 They'll look at the house. Then they'll buy it.
5 He'll wait until the car breaks down. Then he'll sell it.
6 Mark always reads the reviews. Then he buys a book.
7 Mary will go to Spain. Then she'll start her new job.
8 The painting will be finished. Then you'll come back home.
9 They'll destroy the park. Then they'll stop cutting down the trees.
10 She's determined to win the championship. Then she'll leave school.
11 He left the party. Then there was the accident.
12 He'll meet you here. Then you'll leave together.
13 Robert will get his exam results. Then he'll look for a job.
14 We'll go to the cinema. Then we'll have dinner.
15 You must finish that work. Then we'll go for a swim.

4 Join the sentences

Join the sentences using after.
Example:
We'll see the film. Then we'll eat.
We'll eat after we've seen the film.

1 Alan will get married. Then he'll return to work.
2 The summer will be over. Then we'll have a holiday.
3 John swims every morning. Then he has breakfast.
4 My brother took those photographs of the family. Then he left home.
5 The train left. Then Joan got to the station.
6 There was a long, dry summer. Then the rains came.
7 She read the book. Then she saw the film.

8 They lived in Rome. Then they lived in Istanbul.
9 He left for work. Then she arrived.
10 I'll go for a walk. Then I'll start painting the house.
11 Robert heard the news. Then he wrote Jane a letter.
12 Alice will do the shopping. Then she'll get ready for the party.
13 David will restore the painting. Then he'll try to sell it.
14 Everyone will finish dinner. Then we'll tell them the news.
15 Tom left Susan. Then she burnt his books.

5 Complete the dialogue

Jenny and Tom are arranging when to meet. Complete the dialogue with before *or* after.

Jenny: When will you come to see me?
Tom: (**1**) .... I go on holiday. Then I can tell you my plans.
Jenny: But it will have to be (**2**) .... I've come back from Paris. When do you go on holiday?
Tom: In about three weeks. That will be (**3**) .... I go to the football championship. I can't miss that.
Jenny: I used to go to football matches. But that was (**4**) .... I met Richard. He doesn't like football.
Tom: That's a pity. I always enjoy the fun (**5**) .... your team wins the game.
Jenny: What if your team loses? Anyway, will you see me first, (**6**) .... you go to the football championship or later (**7**) .... you've lost the game?
Tom: We won't lose. The last time we lost was (**8**) .... the captain was injured.
Jenny: That was last year! You could say the last time you won was (**9**) .... the captain was injured.
Tom: I'll come and see you (**10**) .... I see the match. Then we won't know the result and so we can't quarrel about it.

UNIT 44 Conjunctions 3: Purpose
to / in order to; so that / in order that

FORM

TO / IN ORDER TO
Positive
main clause + infinitive +...
main clause + *in order to* + infinitive +...
Look at these sentences.
*John moved to another house **to live** near Jane.*
*John moved to another house **in order to** live near Jane.*
Note:
We can use the infinitive to show purpose. This is the most common use in the positive form.
Negative
main clause + *in order + not +* infinitive +...
In the negative we only use the *in order to* form.
*John moved to another house **in order not to** live near Jane.*

SO THAT / IN ORDER THAT
Main clause + *so that / in order that* + clause
Look at these sentences:
*John moved to another house **so that** his old mother could visit him easily.*
*John moved to another house **in order that** his old mother **could** visit him easily.*
After *so that / in order that*, we usually use a modal verb.
If the main verb is present or present perfect, we use *can, will, may*.
If the main verb is past, we use *could, would, might*.

USE

1   We use these clauses to say why someone did something.
2   *to / in order to*
We use this form when the person is doing something for him / herself.
John went to the museum to see the jewellery from ancient Rome.
Here John wanted to see the jewellery.

3   *so that / in order that*
We use this form when the subject after *so that* or *in order that* is different from the subject in the other part of the sentence.
*John moved to another house so that **his old mother** could visit him easily.*
Here John moved to another house for his old mother.

---

1 Match the parts

Match the parts of these sentences. The first one has been done for you.

1   They stayed late ◄─────────────
2   Mary will buy the tickets
3   Fred did a lot of tennis practice ──────►
4   Janet works hard
5   I've come early
6   I've bought you a bicycle
7   I've bought a bicycle
8   He goes to that restaurant
9   Her father will give Joan a car

a)   to get a good seat for the game.
b)   so that his friends will think he is rich.
c)   to finish the work on time.
d)   to entertain his friends.
e)   so that you will do some exercise.
f)   in order to win the important tennis match.
g)   so that her boss will give her more money.
h)   to get some practice for the exam.
i)   so that John can go to the theatre with her.

2 Join the sentences

Join the sentences together with so that *or* in order that.
Example:
I wrote that letter. He will know I enjoyed his performance.
I wrote that letter so that he will know I enjoyed his performance.

I wrote that letter in order that he will know I enjoyed his performance.

1   I gave him some money. He can buy some food.
2   She read her baby son a story. He would go to sleep.
3   Jane has saved a lot of money. Her parents have a good holiday.
4   He gave the paintings to the museum. Everyone can see them.

5 She's putting the fire on. The guests will be warm.
6 We'll go to the airport early. You won't miss your flight.
7 I'll phone. You know I arrived safely.
8 He bought her an expensive ring. She would marry him.
9 Lydia gave Sam the book. He would study for his exam.
10 She always plants lots of flowers. The garden looks lovely.

3 Join the sentences

Join the sentences with to *or in* order to.
Example:
John works hard. He wants to please his boss.
John works hard to please his boss.
John works hard in order to please his boss.

1 She drove very fast. She wanted to arrive early.
2 They bought expensive tickets for the play. They wanted to get good seats.
3 He read the book three times. He wanted to be certain of the murderer.
4 She always goes to Zurich in May. She wants to have Swiss asparagus.
5 He came early. He didn't want to miss the beginning of the game.
6 He's going to Germany. He wants to see Eva, his future wife.
7 They've bought a house near the sea. They want to go sailing.
8 He plays his music loudly. He wants to annoy the neighbours.
9 I stayed at the party late. I didn't want to go home with Mary.
10 She sold her jewels. She wanted to get some money.

4 Complete the sentences

Complete the sentences with so that *or* to.
Example:
Walter's renting a car *to* go to York on Sunday.
Walter's renting the car *so that* Peter will take him to York on Sunday.

1 Jenny's flying to Australia .... see her brother.
2 He's cutting down the trees .... build some expensive houses there.
3 They're moving house .... their son can live near his friends.
4 They've bought that land .... make a children's playground.
5 He caught the early train .... his friend would be able to meet him.
6 They worked during their holidays .... get enough money to buy a motorbike.
7 The firemen closed all the doors .... the fire wouldn't spread.
8 The rail company put on extra trains .... more people could go to the exhibition.
9 Edward played music .... relax while he worked.
10 He had a mobile phone .... people could always phone him in an emergency.

5 Answer the questions

Answer the questions using so that, to *or in* order not to.
Example:
Why did you shout loudly? (John could hear me)
So that John could hear me.
Why did you come early? (finish this work)
To finish this work.
Why did you run away? (not meet Fred)
In order not to meet Fred.

1 Why did the policeman stop those cars? (the children could cross the road safely)
2 Why are you writing that letter? (complain of the bad service)
3 Why are you coming in September instead of October? (be at my brother's wedding)
4 Why is she working late? (the boss will give her a better job)
5 Why are you going to Spain in March? (not be there in the tourist season)
6 Why are you borrowing his security case? (not lose these important documents)
7 Why are you playing that loud music? (annoy the neighbours)
8 Why are you giving your son a car? (he not borrow mine)
9 Why are you putting that picture on that wall? (everyone can see it easily)
10 Why are you having the party? (celebrate my good exam results)

Conjunctions 4: Reason
because

FORM AND USE

1 We use *because* to show the reason why someone does something.
*He did the work quickly **because** he wanted to go home early.*
2 The tense in the reason (*because...*) part of the sentence does not depend on the tense for the main activity.
*John **moved** to another house because he **wanted** to live near Jane.*
Here the tenses in both parts of the sentence are the same.
But:
*John **moved** to another house because he **wants** to live near Jane.*
Here the tenses are different.
3 We use the simple past tense, if the reason is something that is past.
*John wants to buy a new car because the old car **broke** down last week.*
(The reason happened in the past.)
*John moved to another house because he **wanted** to live near Jane.*
(We don't know if the reason is still true.)
4 We use the present simple tense if the reason is still true.
*John moved to another house because he **wants** to live near Jane.*
5 We use a tense for the future if the reason is something in the future.
*John is buying travellers' cheques because he **is going to travel** round the world next month.*

---

1 **Match the sentences**

Match the sentences. Then say which kind of reason is given (A) in the past (B) still true (C) for the future. The first one has been done for you.

1 Mavis went shopping.
2 John went to see Bill.
3 I live near the sea.
4 I prefer to travel by ship.
5 I didn't go to the restaurant.
6 Jon looked after her cat.
7 Peter joined the swimming club.
8 Anne saved her money.
9 Alan accepted the job.
10 He liked the painting.
11 I couldn't go to the cinema.

a) She was going on holiday. ☐
b) I like the sound of the waves. ☐
c) It was a picture of the house where he was born. ☐
d) He needs the money. ☐
e) She wants to buy a new coat. ☐
f) It is very relaxing on board. ☐
g) I didn't have any money. ☐
h) He will need Bill to help him with his work. ☐
i) I spend too much eating out. ☐
j) He likes swimming a lot. ☐
k) She wanted to buy a new car. ☐

---

2 **Join the sentences**

Join these sentences using because.
Example:
I refused to do any more. The man in charge was rude.
I refused to do any more because the man in charge was rude.

1 John comes home late these days. He's unhappy at home.
2 I saw that film twice. The actress is very good.
3 I was very polite to him. He will be my boss next month.
4 You'll have to go without me. I'm not ready yet.
5 The holiday is costing a lot of money. You want to stay in the best hotel.
6 I'm going to India next month. I've got some work there.
7 They can't sell that house. It's in a bad position.
8 You should do more exercise. You're too fat.
9 I'm going home early. I'm tired.
10 The train's delayed. There were cows on the line.
11 Paul is studying astronomy. He wants to go to the moon.
12 They have a very big dog. It frightens off burglars.
13 He climbed through the window. He lost his keys.
14 Simon's got two jobs. He needs the money.
15 Pauline is studying French. She wants to marry Pierre.

UNITS 38–39

Join these sentences together with who, which *or without a relative pronoun (ø).*

1 John owns that car. The car was stolen.
2 Mary's friend is very rich. She lives in the large house on the hill.
3 The park is dangerous at night. The park closes at 6 o'clock.
4 Give me the book. Mary gave you the book.
5 I can't buy that radio. I want the radio.
6 The woman is very old. The woman lives in that house.
7 He likes the white houses. The white houses are in southern Spain.
8 It's a very attractive place. I bought it last year.
9 He caught the train. The train is the quickest to London.
10 The boy climbed the tree. The tree is the tallest in the park.
11 The boy climbed to the top of the tree. The boy is very strong.
12 I thought that exercise was very difficult. The teacher gave us the exercise.

UNITS 40–41

A *Complete these sentences with* whose, of whom *or* of which.

13 They don't like the girl .... brother is the winner of the dance competition.
14 I've met a lot of Chinese people, many .... were very clever.
15 I don't want to buy oranges, many .... are bad.
16 That's the woman .... car was stolen.
17 The trees, many .... have already been cut down, were dying.

B *Replace* in which *and* on which *with* when *or* where.

18 That was the day on which he finished university.
19 I'm looking forward to a time in which I can practise playing my guitar.
20 Is that the park in which your father and mother met?

21 I stood on the hill on which they put the flag.
22 She was born in the year in which the first man walked on the moon.
23 That's the house in which the murder happened.

UNITS 42–43
Write the verbs in brackets in the correct tense.

24 I'll see her when I (be) in Athens.
25 I saw her while I (sit) outside the café.
26 When I pass my exam, I (get) a good job.
27 They'll meet you after they (see) the film.
28 After he arrives home, he always (have) a bath.
29 He wrote to his aunt before he (visit) her.

UNIT 44
Join these sentences with so that *or* to.

30 He's working hard now. He wants to get a better job.
31 David stayed at home. Then Jane could go to the play.
32 He put the picture in the study. Then everyone could see it.
33 She does exercise every day. She wants to keep fit.
34 He caught the early train. He wanted to meet Joan for lunch.

UNIT 45

A *Put the verb in the correct tense according to the letter given*
(A = in the past, B = still true, C = for the future).

35 I went to that doctor because he (be) very good. (B)
36 They didn't like the restaurant because the food (be) bad. (A)
37 They've moved to the suburbs because that area of town (become) very pleasant when the new park is opened. (C)
38 I bought that picture now because it (become) more valuable in the next few years. (C)
39 Don't play by the river because it (be) dangerous. (A)

UNITS 1–11

A *Write the verbs in brackets in the correct tenses.*

1 Jane (go) to work every day by train.
2 Tom (live) in Stockholm.
3 Mary (write) a new book at the moment.
4 Where (study) your daughter now?
5 I often (play) in the park, but today I (walk) by the canal.
6 He (live) in Rome, but at the moment he (stay) with friends in Poland.
7 She never (go) to the theatre.
8 She (act) in a play for the local actors' group.
9 Don't tell her about John. She (not like) him.
10 What (do) you last Monday evening?
11 Jane (see) the film at the local cinema last Saturday.
12 John (not do) well in the exam last month.
13 They met while they (walk) in the park.
14 It's not true, John (not talk) to Jennifer when the director came into the room.
15 I (read) a book last night, but I (not finish) it.
16 I (listen) to the radio when Alan (phone).
17 (Go) you swimming every day when you were a child, Daddy?
18 They (cycle) to work when they were young, but they don't now.
19 Charles always went to the park, but I (not go) there.
20 I (live) here for forty years, and I'm not moving now!
21 (See) you that film at the Apollo cinema this week?
22 He (not go) on holiday yet.
23 (ever be) you to Rome?
24 Yes, I have. I (go) there in August 1995.
25 (see) you the Empire State Building?
26 No, I (never be) to New York.
27 Really? I (go) there last year.
28 I (be) in India next June.
29 He (see) you at 5.30 this afternoon. Can you wait until then?
30 They (win) the prize next year.
31 The train (leave) at 6.15 a.m.
32 I (see) Mavis next Monday.

UNITS 12–17

A *Complete the text with the correct modal, according to the meaning given in brackets.*

When you are travelling abroad, you (**33**) .... (obligation) make sure you have the right protection.

You (**34**) .... (advice) go to your doctor and he (**35**) .... (future ability) tell you which vaccinations you (**36**) .... (necessity) to have. If he is not sure, you (**37**) .... (possibility) telephone the embassy of the country you intend to visit. The staff (**38**) .... (ability) advise you. You (**39**) .... (obligation) give yourself plenty of time because for some countries you (**40**) .... (necessity) have several vaccinations and these (**41**) .... (advice) not be done together. Children under nine months (**42**) .... (prohibition) be vaccinated, except in very special circumstances. You (**43**) .... (possibility) find that you (**44**) .... (impossibility) enter certain countries if you don't have the proper vaccination certificates.

B *Complete the dialogue with the correct modal, according to the meaning given in brackets.*

Jane: (**45**) .... I go out tonight? (most common form of request)
Mother: No, you (**46**) .... (refusing permission)
Jane: Then (**47**) .... I watch television? (more polite request)
Mother: No, you (**48**) .... (strong prohibition)
Jane: Then what (**49**) .... I do? (possibility)
Mother: You (**50**) .... (obligation) tidy your bedroom!

UNIT 18

A *Complete these sentences with a phrase showing the person or thing is the same.*
Example: John is rich. *So is* Mandy.

51 The United States is a very big country. .... China.
52 Hilary didn't pass her exams. .... Anne.
53 David must go to London on Monday. .... Robert.
54 You shouldn't work so late. .... Alice.

UNITS 19–20

A *Write the verbs in the correct tense.*

55 If he (want) to go to China, he'll have to get a visa.
56 If he (see) her in the garden, he always (talk) to her.
57 If the dog runs away tomorrow, you (be) in trouble.
58 I'd be very happy, if I (live) in New Zealand.
59 If the cats (see) her, they always (follow) her. They were sorry when she died.
60 I (be) angry if they (cut) down those trees next week.

UNIT 21

A *Rewrite these sentences in the passive.*

61 My uncle planted those trees.
62 My friend has written a best-selling novel.
63 Those dogs destroyed my garden.

UNITS 22–23

A *Write these statements and questions in reported speech.*

64 'The doctor will see you on Wednesday,' the secretary told Richard.
65 'Where has Mary put my book?' John asked Daisy.
66 'Is Mr Brown at home?' the policeman asked Mrs Brown.
67 'Don't bring that cat in here!' David's mother told him.

UNIT 24

A *Write the correct question tag.*

68 You can't park here, ...?
69 You went to Paris without me, ...?
70 Cats like milk, ...?

UNIT 25

A *Put in the correct article* (a, an, the *or no article*)

John saw (71) .... strange man standing in (72) .... front of (73) .... big house at (74) .... end of (75) .... street (76) .... man was tall with (77) .... blond hair. He was carrying (78) .... suitcase and (79) .... stick (80) .... stick was very thick (81) .... suitcase seemed to be empty. (82) .... man climbed up to (83) .... window and went into (84) .... house.

UNITS 26–27

A *Write the correct form to show possession and also* this, that, these *or* those.

85 .... book over there belongs to me. It's ....
86 .... book here is .... (Richard) book.
87 Do .... cows in the field over there belong to you? Are they .... cows?
88 No, they aren't. They're .... (the farmer).

UNIT 28

A *Write in* some, any *or* no.

89 There's .... bread in the kitchen.
90 But there isn't .... butter.
91 Have you found .... plates in the cupboard?
92 No. There are .... plates in there. It's empty.

UNITS 29–30

A *Write* many, much, a lot of, few *or* little.

93 How .... is that car?
94 I haven't seen .... flowers in the fields this year.
95 No, there aren't .... flowers this year.
96 It's a bad year for the countryside. I've seen .... birds, and usually I see a lot.
97 It's the weather. There's been .... sun. It's always raining.

UNIT 31

A *Write* fewer, fewest, less, least, more *or* most.

98 I've read .... of the books in that library. I can't find any I like now.
99 Nobody's interested in the game. Not many people came last night. And tonight it was worse. .... came.
100 He was saving his money to help his father. So he always spent .... than his friends. They thought he was mean.

UNIT 32

A *Write the words in the sentences in the correct order, and put in the correct frequency adverb according to the percentage shown.*

101 gathered the at five lions lake (100%) o'clock the near
102 film nowadays see (20%) good you a

UNIT 33–34

A *Write the correct form of the adjective or adverb.*

103 The (old) person in the world died in 1997, aged 122.
104 John worked (hard) than David.
105 This table is (heavy) than the one in your house.
106 Sandra won the music prize. She sang the (beautifully) of all the singers.

UNIT 35–36

A *Write the correct preposition of place or time.*

107 I'll see you .... ten o'clock.
108 He always works late .... the evening.
109 She never drives here. She always comes .... foot.
110 That chair looks fine .... the corner of the room.

UNIT 37

A *Write* very, too *or* enough.

111 That coat was .... expensive, but I bought it because I liked it.
112 The box was .... heavy. John couldn't lift it.
113 Have you got .... money? I can lend you some if you haven't.

UNITS 38–40

A *Join these sentences together using a relative pronoun,* who, which, that, whose *or* of which.

114 Books don't interest me. They were written thirty years ago.
115 The prize went to the actor. He won it last year.
116 I didn't like the film. I saw it last week.
117 Next week he'll visit his aunt. She lives in Oxford.
118 That's the man. His car was stolen.
119 He's a member of the city administration. The chairman of it is an unpleasant man.

UNIT 41

A *Replace the underlined words with* when *or* where.

120 I remember that day fifty years ago <u>on which</u> the cinema was opened.

121 He can't remember the place <u>in which</u> he was born.
122 I'll see him during that month <u>in which</u> I'm on holiday.
123 That's the mountain <u>on which</u> I saw the white leopard.

UNITS 42–43

A *Write the verbs in brackets in the correct tense.*

124 While I (sit) in the garden, my brother was writing a history essay.
125 Send me a card when you (arrive) in Singapore.
126 John will buy a new car before he (get) married.
127 He'll come to see you after he (see) his father.

UNITS 44–45

A *Join these sentences with* so that, to *or* because. *Choose the conjunction according to the definition in brackets at the end of the sentence.*

128 Paul worked hard. He would get a better job. (purpose)
129 Mary studied hard. Her father could be proud of her. (purpose)
130 The dog ran away. The man chased him with a stick. (reason)

Irregular verbs

PRESENT SIMPLE/ INFINITIVE	PAST SIMPLE	PAST PARTICIPLE	PRESENT SIMPLE/ INFINITIVE	PAST SIMPLE	PAST PARTICIPLE
be	was/were	been	leave	left	left
become	became	become	lend	lent	lent
begin	began	begun	let	let	let
bite	bit	bitten	lie	lay	lain
blow	blew	blown	light	lit	lit
break	broke	broken	lose	lost	lost
bring	brought	brought	make	made	made
build	built	built	meet	met	met
buy	bought	bought	pay	paid	paid
catch	caught	caught	put	put	put
choose	chose	chosen	read	read	read
come	came	come	ride	rode	ridden
cut	cut	cut	ring	rang	rung
dig	dug	dug	run	ran	run
do	did	done	say	said	said
draw	drew	drawn	see	saw	seen
drink	drank	drunk	sell	sold	sold
drive	drove	driven	send	sent	sent
eat	ate	eaten	shine	shone	shone
fall	fell	fallen	show	showed	shown
feed	fed	fed	shut	shut	shut
fight	fought	fought	sing	sang	sung
find	found	found	sit	sat	sat
fly	flew	flown	sleep	slept	slept
forget	forgot	forgotten	speak	spoke	spoken
forgive	forgave	forgiven	spend	spent	spent
get	got	got	stand	stood	stood
give	gave	given	steal	stole	stolen
go	went	gone	swim	swam	swum
grow	grew	grown	take	took	taken
hang	hung	hung	teach	taught	taught
have	had	had	tell	told	told
hear	heard	heard	think	thought	thought
hit	hit	hit	throw	threw	thrown
hold	held	held	understand	understood	understood
hurt	hurt	hurt	wake	woke	woken
keep	kept	kept	wear	wore	worn
know	knew	known	win	won	won
lay	laid	laid	write	wrote	written
lead	led	led			

Punctuation and Spelling

Punctuation

CAPITAL LETTERS
We use capital letters for:
1   the word at the beginning of a sentence:
The day started well for John.
It was the best time of the year.
2   whenever we use the first person singular 'I':
I met him in the evening.
*You and **I** must go to the theatre together soon.*
3   with names of people and places, titles of books and journals, days of the week and months:
Gillian Wright
Mount Everest
The Times
Tuesday
June

FULL STOP
We put a full stop
1   at the end of sentences which are statements:
It rained all last night.
2   or imperative forms which are not strong orders:
Come home early.

COMMA
We use a comma when
1   we are connecting two main clauses with *and* or *but*, if the subject is different in each clause:
He left home and went to work.
(No comma – the subject is the same in each clause.)
She left home early, but the train was very late.
(Comma – the subject is different in each clause.)
2   after a subordinate clause:
***When he came home**, he felt very angry.*
3   but not before a subordinate clause:
*He felt very angry **when he came home**.*
4   after an adverbial or prepositional phrase:
***On Sunday**, I'll meet Anne.*
5   but not before an adverbial or prepositional phrase:
*I'll meet Anne **on Sunday**.*

Spelling

PLURAL NOUNS
Regular forms
1   Most nouns add *s* to the singular when they become plural.
book – books, apple – apples
2   For nouns ending in *ch, sh, s, ss* or *x* in the singular, add *es* to the noun to make the plural form.
watch – watches, wish – wishes, bus – buses, box – boxes
3   For nouns ending in consonant + y in the singular, change *y* to *i* and add *es* to make the plural form.
baby – babies

4   For nouns ending in vowel + *y* in the singular, add *s* to make the plural form.
day – days, monkey – monkeys

Irregular forms
1   Some nouns that end in *o* add *es* to form the plural.
potato – potatoes, tomato – tomatoes, hero – heroes, etc.
2   Some nouns that end in *f* or *fe*, change the *f* to *v* and add *es*.
calf – calves, half – halves, wife – wives, etc.
3   There are seven nouns which change completely.
foot – feet, goose – geese, tooth – teeth, man – men, woman – women, mouse – mice, louse – lice
4   Two common nouns add *en* to form the plural.
child – children, ox – oxen
5   Some nouns do not have a different form for the plural.
sheep – sheep, deer – deer, aircraft – aircraft

DOUBLING CONSONANTS
Words with one syllable
Verbs and adjectives that end in vowel + consonant
(e.g. *to stop, to plan, wet, thin*) double the consonant before adding an ending.
For verbs -*ed* or -*ing*:
stop – stopped – stopping
plan – planned – planning
rub – rubbed – rubbing
for adjectives -*er* or -*est*:
wet – wetter – wettest
thin – thinner – thinnest
big – bigger – biggest

Words with more than one syllable
1 For verbs that end in vowel + consonant
(e.g. *prefer, begin, visit, develop*)
1   We double the consonant when the final syllable is stressed.
*pre**fer** – preferred – preferring*
*be**gin** – beginning*
(*begin* is an irregular verb in the past)
*per**mit** – permitted – permitting*
*re**gret** – regretted – regretting*
2   When the final syllable is not stressed, we do not double the final consonant.
visit – visited – visiting
remember – remembered – remembering
happen – happened – happening
3   In British English, for verbs ending in *l*, we put *ll* before -*ed* or -*ing*.
travel – travelled – travelling

Note:
In American English, they do not double the *l*.
travel – traveled – traveling